W9-BZI-914

THE LONGMANS MINIATURE ARROW SCORE SERIES

ROMANTIC AND MODERN VIOLIN CONCERTOS

EDITED AND DEVISED BY

ALBERT E. WIER

LONGMANS, GREEN AND CO.

NEW YORK

WIER

ROMANTIC AND MODERN VIOLIN CONCERTOS

COPYRIGHT · 1940

BY LONGMANS, GREEN AND CO., INC.

ALL RIGHTS RESERVED, INCLUDING THE RIGHT TO REPRODUCE THIS BOOK, OR ANY PORTION THEREOF, IN ANY FORM

FIRST EDITION

The system of arrow signals, employed in this work to enable those unacquainted with the art of score reading to follow the instrumental outline, is the subject of a pending application for Letters Patent of the United States owned by Albert E. Wier.

MT
85
.W5
R74

BRIAR CLIFF COLLEGE
LIBRARY
SIOUX CITY, IOWA

PRINTED IN THE UNITED STATES OF AMERICA

THE ARROW SYSTEM OF SCORE READING

The arrow system is a device designed to provide those who have not studied the art of score reading with a means for following the melodic and structural outlines of chamber or orchestral works. It is so simple in both principle and application that anyone who can read ordinary instrumental music can readily follow the succession of arrow signals that guide the eye from staff to staff as the various instruments in the score take precedence over others in carrying or developing the melodic and structural outlines.

In using the arrow system for score reading, however, it must be borne in mind that the parts for instruments such as the clarinet, English horn, French horn, trumpet, etc., are usually transposed in the score, and are therefore written in a different key from that in which the parts for the stringed instruments are placed ; also that the C clef is used for the viola, and at times for the violoncello and trombone.

It will be noted that, while a single arrow is used as a guide when the melodic line rests in only one instrument, two, three and even four arrows at the same measure but on different staves, are sometimes necessary to indicate the participation of more than one instrument in the structural development of the composition at that particular point. In such instances the reader can concentrate his attention on any one of the staves on first reading, and gradually acquire skill in reading all the arrowed staves simultaneously as he becomes more proficient in "following the arrow."

An arrow is placed with its point slanting down when it is intended to indicate one particular staff ; when placed between two staves with its point horizontal, , the indication is that the instrument represented on the staff above and the one on the staff below the arrow are of interest to the reader.

In volumes containing concertos for piano or for violin with orchestral accompaniment, the piano or the violin solo staves are distinguished from the instrumental accompaniment staves by a hand ( ) signal ; the points of interest in the orchestral passages are indicated by the usual arrow signals.

ALBERT E. WIER

22580

INDEX

LIST OF RECORDINGS

The recordings listed below of the violin concertos contained in this volume are chiefly of American manufacture, and accordingly readily procurable in the United States. They are listed alphabetically by the names of the artists who perform them. The names of the recording companies are abbreviated in parentheses as follows:

(C) Columbia	(V) Victor
Brahms, Johannes	
Concerto in D major, Op. 77	Heifetz (V) Kreisler (V) Szigeti (C)
Double Concerto in A minor, Op. 102	Thibaud and Casals (V)
Bruch, Max	
Concerto No. 1 in G minor, Op. 26	Campoli (C) Menuhin (V)
Dvořák, Antonín	
Concerto in A minor, Op. 53	Menuhin (V)
Glazounoff, Alexander	
Concerto in A minor, Op. 82	Heifetz (V)
Lalo, Édouard	
Symphonie Espagnole	Hubermann (C) Menuhin (V)
Saint-Saëns, Camille	
Concerto in B minor, Op. 61	Merckel (V)
Tschaikowsky, Peter Ilich	
Concerto in D major, Op. 35	Elman (V) Heifetz (V) Hubermann (C)
Vieuxtemps, Henri	
Concerto No. 4 in D minor, Op. 31	Heifetz (V)
Wieniawski, Henri	
Concerto in D minor, Op. 22	Heifetz (V)

JOHANNES BRAHMS

CONCERTO in D major, Op. 77 *Score P. 7*

This work, dedicated to Joseph Joachim, was probably begun during the latter months of 1878, after Brahms and Karl Goldmark had made a tour of Italy. The composer held several conferences with Joachim regarding technical matters in connection with the solo part, but in the end, according to Karl Geiringer, eminent musicologist and one of Brahms' biographers, he made very few changes in accordance with Joachim's suggestions; as stated by Geiringer, proof is to be found in the manuscript of the violin part which, marked with the great violinist's emendations, is preserved in the Prussian State Library. It was probably Brahms' fear and dislike of uselessly ornamental passages so frequently added in violin concertos to display technical skill that impelled him to follow no judgment except his own. Authorities are agreed that Brahms has amply demonstrated the fact that his knowledge of violin technique was more than adequate, and that he affords all the opportunities necessary for dignified display of virtuoso powers in the cadenza.

The concerto was first performed in public on New Year's Day, 1879, at a Gewandhaus Concert in Leipzig with Joachim as soloist. It was calmly but not enthusiastically received; Joachim also played it in London at the Crystal Palace on Feb. 22, 1879, and again with the Royal Philharmonic Society (London) on March 5th of the same year; it was well received on both occasions. That the work has been and is now highly regarded by all really great violin virtuosos is amply evidenced by the fact that it has been in their repertories, almost without exception, ever since it was published in October, 1879; the list of violinist-composers who have written cadenzas for it includes Joachim, Halir, Heermann, Singer, Ondřiček, Auer, Marteau, Zajic, Aulin, Besekirsky and Schradieck. The great pianist-composer, Ferruccio Busoni, also was sufficiently enthused by the work to write a cadenza for it.

The most striking critique of the work is to be found in Walter Niemann's biography of Brahms: "This much we may say: even though it neither is nor could have been in the style of Beethoven, yet, of all modern violin concertos it certainly stands nearest to Beethoven both in the charm and significance of its content, which is as earnest as it is attractive, and in its genuine, powerful virility. Just as Spohr, Mendelssohn and Bruch may be said to have composed the feminine romantic German violin concertos, so Brahms may be said to have written the masculine one."

Concerto in D major, Op. 77

5
7
6
8
Fl.
Hb.
Kl.
Fg.
(D)
Hr.
(E)
Tr.
(D)
Pk.
S. Vl.
Vl.
Br.
Vo.
Kb.
40
50
60
70
poco cresc.
p cresc.
dol.
p dol.
a 2.

9
80
Fl.
Hb.
Kl.
Fg.
(D) Hr. (E)
Tr. (D)
Pk.
S. Vl.
Vl.
Br.
Vc.
Kb.
dim.
f marc.
f
11
10
12
90
fp

13
15
14
16
100
110
Hr. (D)
Pk.
S. Vl.
Vl.
Br.
Vo.
Kb.
Hb.
Kl.
Fg.
Fl.
Tr. (D)
f marc.
fp
cresc.
fpp
pp
p
f

17
Fl.
Hb.
Kl.
Fg.
p
dim.
(D)
Hr.
(E)
dim.
Tr.
(D)
Pk.
tr
S. Vl.
dim.
Vl.
Br.
Vc.
dim.
Kb.
18
120
pp
a 2.
p
19
muta D. in E.
espress.
20
130
rit.

21
a tempo
140
Fg.
Hr. (D)
S. Vl.
Vl.
Br.
Vo.
Kb.
pp
p espress
pizz.
23
cresc.
fp marc.
170
mf marc.
22
150
dolce
arco
p dolce
160
espress.
24
Fl.
Hr. (E)
fp
mf

25
180
Fl.
Fg.
Hr. (E)
S. Vl.
p dolce
Vl.
Br.
Vo.
Kb.
cresc.
26
190
Fl.
Kl.
Fg.
pp
S. Vl.
Vl.
Br.
Vo.
Kb.
200
Hb.
ppp
27
Fl.
Hb.
Kl.
Fg.
(D) Hr. (E)
Tr. (D)
Pk.
pizz.
a 2.
28
210
Kl.
Fg.
Hr. (D)
p dolce
arco

29
220
Fl.
Hb.
Kl.
Fg.
(D)
Hr.
(E)
Tr.
(D)
Pk.
S. Vl.
Vl.
Br.
Vo.
Kb.
p
dim.
p dolce lusingando
pizz.
30
230
pp
arco
31
240
250
arco
pp dim.
mf
f
32
260
ff

S. Vl.
Vl.
cresc.
Br.
Vo.
Kb.
f
270
Fl.
fp
Hb.
Kl.
Fg.
Hr. (E)
280
(D) Hr. (E)
Tr. (D)
Pk.
a 2.
34
ff
36
290
E muta in D
pizz.
pf
p

37

Fl.
Hb.
Kl.
Fg.
Hr. (D)
Vl.
Br.
Vo.
Kb.

pf
pf
pf
pf
p
arco
p
arco
p
mp
pizz.
mp
pizz.
p

300
p
Kl.
Fg.
Hr. (D)
Vl.
Br.
Vo.
Kb.
dim.
dim.
pp
arco
p
dim.
pp
dim.
arco
pp
dim.

38

Kl.
Fg.
S. Vl.
poco f espressivo
Vl.
arco
p
Br.
pizz.
arco
Vo.
p
pizz.
Kb.
p

310
tranquillo
p dolce
Hb.
Kl.
p
Fg.
tranquillo
S. Vl.
p leggiero ma espressivo (grazioso)
simile
Vl.
Br.
Vo.
Kb.
tranquillo

41
340
43
Fl.
Hb.
Kl.
Fg.
(D)
Hr.
(E)
Tr.
(D)
Pk.
S. Vl.
Vl.
Br.
Vo.
Kb.
a 2.
f marc.
f
ff
fp
fp marc.
42
44
più f
p cresc.
cresc.
mf cresc.
Viol.
360

45
47
46
48
370
380
Fl.
Hb.
Kl.
Fg.
(D) Hr. (E)
Tr. (D)
Pk.
S. Vl.
Vl.
Br.
Vc.
Kb.
trem
fpp
mf
pp
fp
p cresc.
cresc.
poco rit.

49
a tempo
Fl.
Hb.
Kl.
Fg.
(D)
Hr.
(E)
Tr.
(D)
Pk.
S. Vl.
Vl.
Br.
Vc.
Kb.
ff a tempo
51
p dol.
dolce
arco
pp
50
390
fp dim.
pizz.
52
400
dol.
cresc.
fp marc.

53
410
S. Vl.
Vl.
mf marc.
Br.
Vc.
Kb.
pizz.
f
54
420
Hb.
Kl.
Fg.
fp
p
a 2
poco cresc.
55
430
Fl.
Hr. (D)
pp
arco
56
440
Tr. (D)
Pk.
dol.

57
59
58
60
450
460
Fl.
Hb.
Kl.
Fg.
(D)
Hr.
(E)
Tr.
(D)
Pk.
S. Vl.
Vl.
Br.
Vc.
Kb.
pizz.
arco
espress.
dol.
p dol.
dim.
p lusingando

61
470
Kl.
(D)
Hr.
(E)
S. Vl.
Vl.
Br.
Vc.
Kb.
pp
dim.
480
arco
62
f
mf
63
500
Fl.
Hb.
Fg.
Tr. (D)
Pk.
ff
64

65
66
67
68
510
520
Fl.
Hb.
Kl.
Fg.
(D)
Hr.
(E)
Tr.
(D)
Pk.
S. Vl.
Vl.
Br.
Vc.
Kb.
fp
f
ff
a 2
Cadenz.
tr

69
tranquillo
530
Fg.
Hr. (D)
S. Vl.
p dol.
Vl.
pp
Br.
Vo.
Kb.
pizz.
tranquillo
540
Fl.
Hb.
Kl.
(D)
Hr.
(E)
dol.
espress.
arco
70
dim.
550
poco a poco cresc.
71
string. poco a poco
p cresc.
Tr. (D)
Pk.
cresc. e string. poco a poco
string. poco a poco
72
animato
560
fp
cresc.

Fl.
Hb.
Kl.
Fg.
(D)
Hr.
(E)
Tr.
(D)
Pk.
S. Vl.
Vl.
Br.
Vc.
Kb.
cresc.
mf

II.

Adagio.
2 Flöten.
2 Hoboen.
2 Klarinetten in B.
2 Fagotte.
2 Hörner in F.
Solo-Violine.
Violine I.
Violine II.
Bratsche.
Violoncell.
Kontrabaß.
dolce
p

570
Fl.
Hb.
Kl.
Fg.
a 2.
(D)
Hr.
(E)
Tr.
(D)
Pk.
S. Vl.
Vl.
Br.
Vc.
Kb.
f
tr

10
20
Fl.
Hb.
Kl.
Fg.
Hr.
(F)
pp
p
dim.

77
79
78
80
30
40
Fl.
Hb.
Kl.
Fg.
Hr. (F)
S. Vl.
Vl.
Br.
Vo.
Kb.
p poco cresc.
p cresc.
p dolce
p dol.
arco
pizz.

81
50
Fl.
Hb.
Kl.
Fg.
Hr. (F)
S. Vl.
Vl.
Br.
Vo.
Kb.
arco
p

83
60
Fl.
Hb.
Kl.
Fg.
Hr. (F)
S. Vl.
dol.
Vl.
Br.
Vo.
Kb.
p

82
poco a poco più largamente
Fl.
Hb.
Kl.
Fg.
Hr. (F)
S. Vl.
f espress.
Vl.
Br.
Vo.
Kb.
p cresc.
poco f
poco a poco f più largamente

84
Fg.
S. Vl.
Vl.
Br.
Vo.
Kb.
p

85
87
S. Vl.
Vl.
Br.
Vo.
Kb.
Fg.
cre
cresc.
scen
do
86
Hr. (F)
dim.
calando
dim. molto
dolce
Tempo I.
Fl.
Hb.
Kl.
dol.
88
90
espress.
pizz.
poco a poco
poco a poco cre.

89
poco cre
scen
mp
cresc.
Fl.
Hb.
Kl.
Fg.
Hr. (F)
S. Vl.
Vl.
Br.
Vo.
Kb.
91
p
dol.
dolce
arco
pp
dim.
90
do
espress. dolce
92
110
pp
dim.

III.

Allegro giocoso, ma non troppo vivace.

2 Flöten.
2 Hoboen.
2 Klarinetten in A.
2 Fagotte.
4 Hörner 1. 2. in D. 3. 4. in E.
2 Trompeten in D.
Pauken in D. A.
Solo-Violine.
Violine I.
Violine II.
Bratsche.
Violoncell.
Kontrabaß.

f sf pf poco f

Fl. Hb. Kl. Fg. (D) Hr. (E) Tr. (D) Pk. S. Vl. Vl. Br. Vc. Kb.

94

S. Vl. Vl. Br. Vc. Kb.

Fl. Hb. Kl. Fg. (D) Hr. (E) Pk. S. Vl. Vl. Br. Vc. Kb.

f ben marcato
f ben marcat
ben marc. sf
in D. A.
10

96

Fl. Hb. Kl. Fg. (D) Hr. (E) Tr. (D) Pk. S. Vl. Vl. Br. Vc. Kb.

pizz.
p

97
99
98
100
Fl.
Hb.
Kl.
Fg.
(D)
Hr.
(E)
Tr.
(D)
Pk.
S. Vl.
Vl.
Br.
Vo.
Kb.
marc.
cresc.
arco
a 2

101
40
Fl.
Hb.
Kl.
Fg.
Hr. (D)
Pk.
S. Vl.
p leggiero
Vl.
Br.
Vc.
Kb.
legg.
pizz.
103
(D) Hr. (E)
Tr. (D)
cresc.
102
50
cresc.
104
60
ff energicamente
arco
ff marc.

BRIAR CLIFF COLLEGE
LIBRARY
22580

109
111
90
Fl.
Hb.
Kl.
Fg.
a 2
(D)
Hr.
(E)
Tr.
(D)
Pk.
S. Vl.
Vl.
Br.
Vo.
Kb.
110
112
100
dim.

113
120
S. Vl.
Vl.
Br.
Vo.
Kb.
Fl.
Kl.
Fg.
pizz.
arco
p dol.
pp
teneramente
115
130
dcl.
dol.
Hb.
Hr.
(D)
(E)
Tr.
Pk.
114
pdol.
più p
pp dolce
dcl.
116
cresc.
espress.

117
118
119
120
140
150
160
a 2
Fl.
Hb.
Kl.
Fg.
Hr. (D)
Hr. (E)
Tr. (D)
Pk.
S. Vl.
Vl.
Br.
Vc.
Kb.
pizz.
arco
cresc.
ff marc.
F

170
121
Fl.
Hb.
Kl.
Fg.
(D)
Hr.
(E)
Tr.
(D)
Pk.
S. Vl.
Vl.
Br.
Vo.
Kb.
180
123
122
a 2
124
pizz.

125
190
Fl.
Hb.
Kl.
Fg.
S. Vl.
Vl.
arco
Br.
Vo.
Kb.
cresc.
127
Hr.
(D)
(E)
Tr.
Pk.
marc.
126
200
f ben marc.
mf cresc.
p cresc.
128
210
ff

129
130
131
132
220
230
Fl.
Hb.
Kl.
Fg.
(D) Hr. (E)
Tr. (D)
Pk.
S. Vl.
Vl.
Br.
Vc.
Kb.
cresc.
legg.
pizz.
più p

133
240
Fl.
Hb.
Kl.
Fg.
(D)
Hr.
(E)
Tr.
(D)
Pk.
S. Vl.
Vl.
pp
pizz.
Br.
Vo.
b.
135
Hr.
(D)
p marc.
f
Kb.
260
cresc.
energicamente
134
arco
250
cresc.
136

137
139
138
140
Fl.
Hb.
Kl.
Fg.
(D) Hr. (E)
Tr. (D)
Pk.
S. Vl.
Vl.
Br.
Vo.
Kb.
p cresc.
pp cresc.
cresc.
p cresc.
arco
Poco più presto.
270
p ma ben marc.
leggiero
pizz.
280
pp legg.
legg.
pizz.

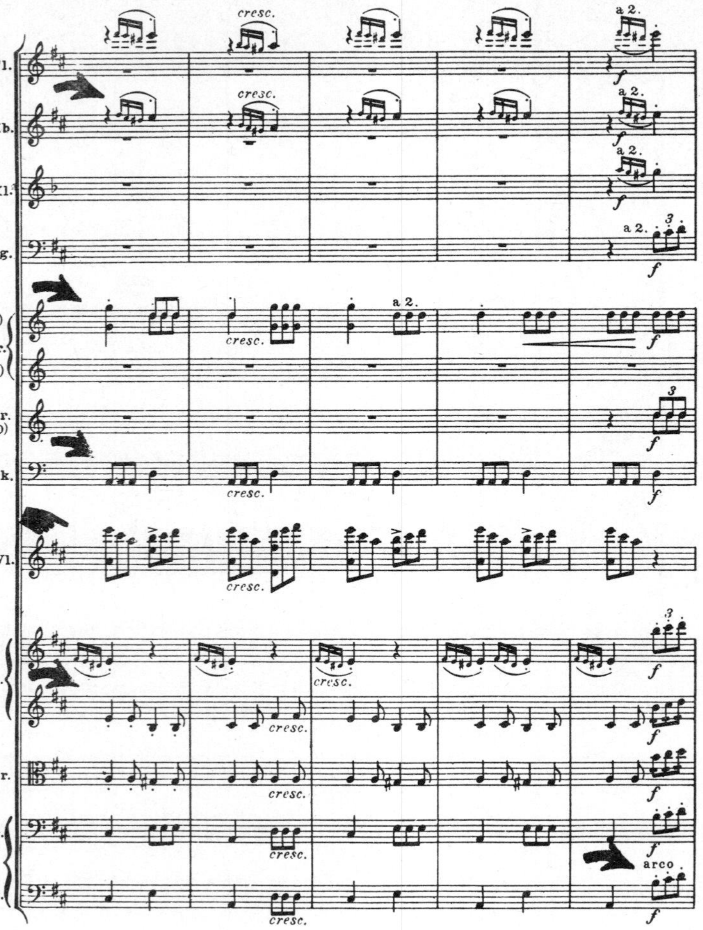

141

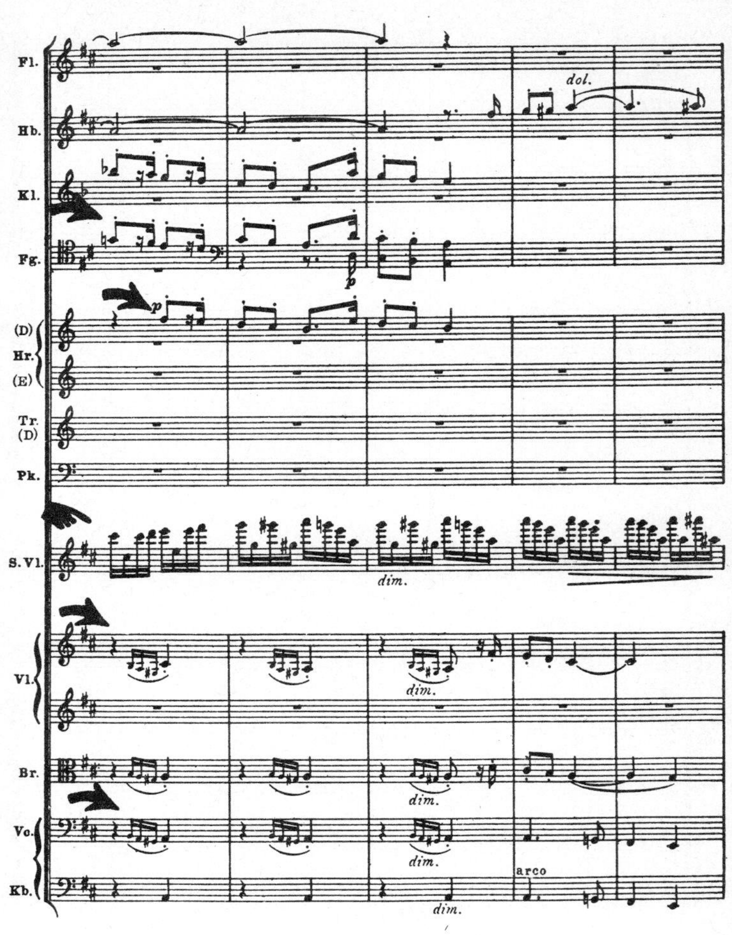

142

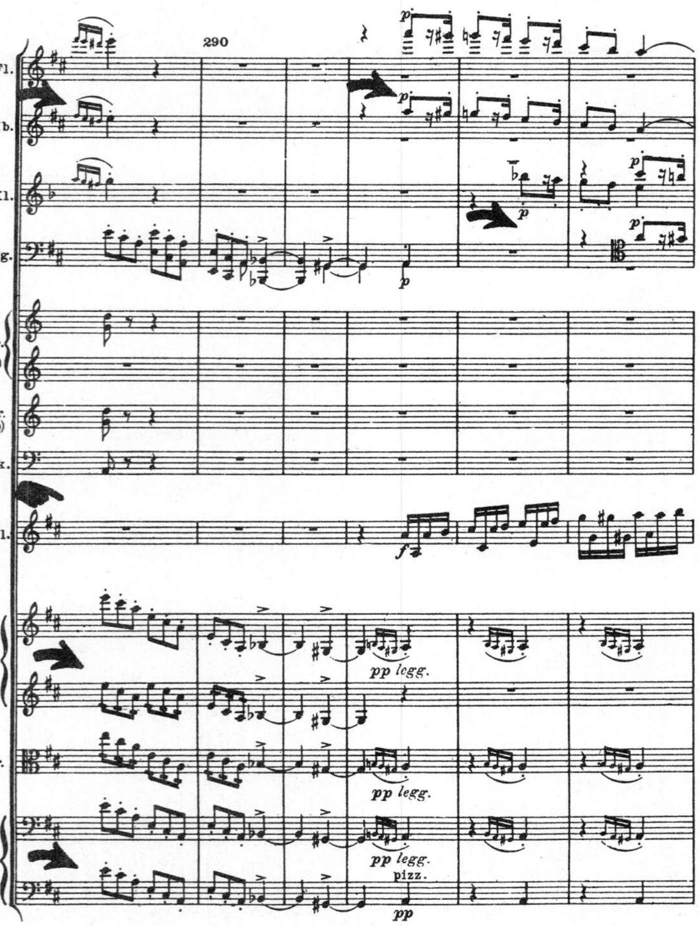

144

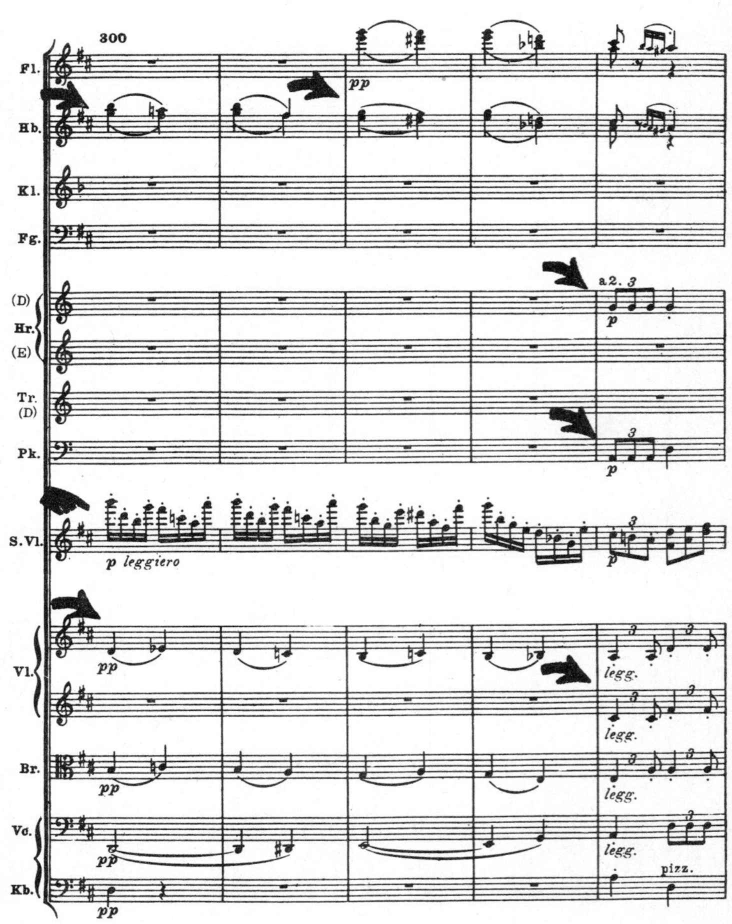

145
147
320
146
310
148
Fl.
Hb.
Kl.
Fg.
(D)
Hr.
(E)
Tr.
(D)
Pk.
S. Vl.
Vl.
Br.
Vo.
Kb.
cresc.
arco
pizz.
a 2.

149
330
Fl.
Hb.
Kl.
Fg.
(D)
Hr.
(E)
Tr.
(D)
Pk.
S. Vl.
Vl.
Br.
Vo.
Kb.
151
340
f dim.
fpp dim.
p dim.
dim.
150
a 2.
f cresc.
152
p dim.
pp
pizz.
arco

JOHANNES BRAHMS

DOUBLE CONCERTO in A minor, Op. 102 *Score P. 46*

This concerto, for violin, violoncello and orchestra, composed in 1887, was the last orchestral work written by Brahms. It seems probable that the composer had definitely decided that it was to be his final contribution to this particular field because he lavished a profusion of beautiful musical ideas upon it, and developed them with even more than his customary care and diligence. It was composed for two of his most intimate friends, Joseph Joachim and Robert Hausmann; they gave the first performance at the Gürzenichsaal in Cologne on Oct. 18, 1887.

According to Walter Niemann, in his critical biography of Brahms, this work was an experiment on the part of the composer in the revival of the *concerto grosso* (orchestral concerto) of the 17th and 18th centuries; in works of this character the orchestral *tutti* are contrasted with a *concertino* for the solo instruments. Niemann also believes that the principal reason why the work is so seldom heard—as is also the case with the Beethoven Triple Concerto for piano, violin and violoncello—is because it demands two performers of consummate technique who must either be thoroughly accustomed to playing together, or have many more opportunities to rehearse, both together and with orchestra, than is usually possible.

The Viennese critic, Eduard Hanslick, wrote that the Brahms double concerto was "the product of a great constructive mind, rather than an irresistible inspiration of creative imagination and invention." Even the composer confided to his intimate friend, Clara Schumann, his lack of ease in its composition because, in his own words: "Indeed, it is not at all the same thing to write for instruments whose nature and timbre one has in one's head, as it were, only from time to time," quite evidently referring to the greater facility with which he could compose for the piano.

1
Double Concerto in A minor, Op. 102
Johannes Brahms
Allegro.
2 Flöten.
2 Hoboen.
2 Klarinetten in A.
2 Fagotte.
2 Hörner in E.
2 Hörner in D.
2 Trompeten in D.
Pauken in E. A.
Solo-Violine.
Solo-Violoncell.
(in modo d'un recitativo, ma sempre in tempo)
Violine I.
Violine II.
Bratsche.
Violoncell.
Baß.
f marc.
Allegro.
2
Solo-Vcl.
cresc.
pizz.
p dol.
dol.
arco
Fl.
Hb.
Kl.
Fg.
Hr. in E
Hr. in D
Solo-Vl.
più f
3
Solo-Vl.
Solo-Vcl.
poco f
cresc.
f sempre più
ff
4
Fl.
Hb.
Kl.
Fg.
Hr. in E
Hr. in D
Trp. in D
Pk.
Vl. I
Vl. II
Br.
Vcl.
B.

5
Fl.
Hb.
Kl.
Fg.
a 2
Hr. in E
Hr. in D
Trp. in D
Pk.
Vl. I
Vl. II
Br.
Vcl.
B.
7
6
70
8
80

9
Fl.
Hb.
Kl.
Fg.
Vl. I
Vl. II
Br.
Vcl.
B.
a 2
90
Hr. in D
Trp. in D
f ben marc.
11
Hr. in E
Pk.
10
12
100

13
Fl.
Hb.
Kl.
Fg.
Hr. in E
Hr. in D
Trp. in D
Pk.
Vl. I
Vl. II
Br.
Vcl.
B.
sf
tr
15
Solo-Vcl.
Solo-Vl.
fp
mp
f
pizz.
arco
14
110
16
120
p
cresc.
poco
a poco
p cresc.

17
130
Fl.
Kl.
Fg.
Solo-Vl.
Solo-Vcl.
Vl.I.
Vl.II.
Br.
Vcl.
B.
pizz.
18
140
Hb.
Hr. in D
più
dim.
19
Hr. in E
dolce
p dol.
20
150
espress.
arco

21
22
23
24
Solo-Vcl.
Br.
Vcl.
B.
Fl.
Kl.
Fg.
Hr. in D
Solo-Vl.
Vl.I.
Vl.II.
Hb.
pizz.
arco
div.
p dol.
p dim.
f marc.

25
27
26
28
Fl.
Kl.
Fg.
Hb.
Solo-Vl.
Solo-Vcl.
Vl. I.
Vl. II.
Br.
Vcl.
B.
Hr. in E
Hr. in D
Trp. in D
dim.
190
200
p ma marc.
a 2
f ben marc.
p
arco
f
f marc.
a 2

29
31
Fl.
Hb.
Kl.
Fg.
Hr. in E
Hr. in D
Trp. in D
Pk.
Vl. I
Vl. II
Br.
Vcl.
B.
a 2
sf
ff
f
30
32
f ben marc.
210

33
220
Hb.
Kl.
Fg.
Hr. in E
Solo-Vl.
Solo-Vcl.
Vl. I
Vl. II
Br.
Vcl.
B.
f
mf
p
pizz.
35
Fl.
dim.
piu p
marc.
p marc.
34
fp
230
divisi arco
arco
36
240
dolce
pp
Hr. in D
p dolce
pizz.
tr

37
Fl.
Hb.
Kl.
Fg.
Hr. in E
Solo-Vl.
Solo-Vcl.
Vl. I
Vl. II
Br.
Vcl.
B.
dolce
marc
p dolce
arco
pizz.
pp
39
260
a 2
ff marc.
Hr. in D
Trp. in D
f
sf
ff
38
250
mf
p cresc.
cresc.
40
ben marc.

41
a 2
Fl.
Hb.
Kl.
Fg.
Vl. I
Vl. II
Br.
Vcl.
B.
270
Kl.
Fg.
Solo-Vcl.
fp
Vl. I
Vl. II
Br.
Vcl.
B.
fpp
pp
42
Solo-Vl.
Solo Vcl.
Vl. I
Vl. II
Br.
Vcl.
B.
Fl.
Kl.
Pk.
280
p
dim.
pp
43
Fl.
Kl.
Fg.
Pk.
cresc.
p cresc.
Solo-Vl.
p cresc. molto
Solo-Vcl.
p cresc. moltò
Vl. I
Vl. II
Br.
Vcl.
B.
cresc. molto
Kl.
Fg.
Hr. in D
mf cresc.
Solo-Vl.
Solo-Vcl.
Vl. I
Vl. II
Br.
Vcl.
B.
f
44
290
a 2
Fl.
Hb.
Kl.
Fg.
Hr. in E
Hr. in D
Trp. in D
Pk.
ff
Solo-Vl.
Solo-Vcl.
Vl. I
Vl. II
Br.
Vcl.
B.
cresc.
ff

45
46
47
48
Fl.
Hb.
Kl.
Fg.
Hr. in E
Hr. in D
Trp. in D
Vl. I
Vl. II
Br.
Vcl.
B.
Solo-Vl.
Solo-Vcl.
a 2
300
310
espress.
pizz.
arco
dim.
p dol.
G.P.

49
50
51
52
320
330
340
350
Fl.
Kl.
Fg.
Hr. in E
Hr. in D
Solo-Vl.
Solo-Vcl.
Vl. I
Vl. II
Br.
Vcl.
B.
Hb.
dim.
pp
p dol.
dol.
legg.
pizz.
arco
p
espress.
sf
a 2
f
mf
fp
p legg.

53
Fl.
Hb.
Kl.
Fg.
Hr. in E
Hr. in D
Solo-Vl.
Solo-Vcl.
Vl. I
Vl. II
Br.
Vcl.
B.
pp
54
più p
dim.
ben marc.
p marc.
55
360
a 2
f marc.
arco
56
Trp. in D
sf

370

Fl.
Hb.
Kl.
a 2
Fg.
Hr. in E
Hr. in D
Trp. in D
Vl.I
sf
3
Vl.II
3
Br.
Vcl.
B.

58

a 2
Fl.
Hb.
Kl.
a 2
a 2
Fg.
Hr. in E
Hr. in D
Trp. in D
f
3
Vl.I
sf
f ben
3
Vl.II
f ben
3
Br.
f
Vcl.
f
B.
f

a 2
Fl.
Hb.
Kl.
Fg.
Hr. in E
Hr. in D
Trp. in D
Pk.
f
Vl.I
marcato
Vl.II
marcato
Br.
Vcl.
B.

60

380
Fl.
Hb.
Kl.
a 2
Fg.
Hr. in E
sf
Hr. in D
sf
Trp. in D
sf
Pk.
sf
Vl.I
sf
Vl.II
sf
Br.
sf
Vcl.
sf
B.
sf

390
Fl.
Hb.
Kl.
Fg.
Hr. in E
Hr. in D
Trp. in D
Pk.
Vl. I
Vl. II
Br.
Vcl.
B.
a 2
sf
ff
f
sempre f
62
64
Solo-Vl.
Solo-Vcl.
fp
pizz.

65
400
Fl.
Kl.
Fg.
Solo-Vl.
Solo-Vcl.
Vl. I
Vl. II
Br.
Vcl.
B.
arco
cresc.
cresc. poco a poco
66
molto cresc.
Hb.
410
67
poco rit.
in tempo
dim.
420
a 2
pizz.
68
Hr. in E
Hr. in D
Trp. in D
Pk.

430
69
Fl.
Hb.
Kl.
Fg.
Hr. in D
Hr. in F
Trp. in D
Pk.
Solo-Vl.
Solo-Vcl.
arco
Vl. I
Vl. II
Br.
Vcl.
B.
70
Andante
2 Flöten
2 Hoboen
2 Klarinetten in A
2 Fagotte
2 Hörner in D
2 Hörner in F
2 Trompeten in D
Solo-Violine
Solo-Violoncell
Violine I
Violine II
Bratsche
Violoncell
Bass
f espress.
poco f ma dolce
71
10
p dolce
dolce
poco f ma dol.
divisi
p dim.
72
20
molto p
cresc.
mf
dim.

73
75
74
76
30
40
50
Fl.
Hb.
Kl.
Fg.
Trp. in D
Solo-Vl.
Solo-Vcl.
Vl. I
Vl. II
Br.
Vcl.
B.
Hr. in F
p dol.
pp
pizz.
arco
dim.
p sempre
p dol. sempre
pp dim.
poco f
pf

77
60
Fl.
Hb.
Kl.
Fg.
Solo-Vl.
Solo-Vcl.
Vl.I
Vl.II
Br.
Vcl.
B.
pizz.
arco
pf
p
dim.
Hr. in F
pp
79
80
mf
tr
f
78
70
mf cresc.
cresc.
Hr. in D
Trp. in D
90
Rmvc.—65

81
83
82
84
Solo-Vl.
Solo-Vcl.
Vl.I.
Vl.II.
Br.
Vcl.
B.
Kl.
Fg.
Fl.
Hb.
Hr. in E
Hr. in D
Trp. in D
Vivace non troppo.
2 Fagotte.
Solo-Violine.
Solo-Violoncell.
Violine I.
Violine II.
Bratsche.
Violoncell.
Baß.
arco
pizz.
dol.
dim.
più p
cresc.

85
Kl.
Solo-Vl.
Solo-Vcl.
Vl.I.
Vl.II.
Br.
Vcl.
B.
Fg.
20
pizz.
87
in tempo
Fl.
ben marc. cresc.
p marc. cresc.
in tempo
86
Hr. in D
dol.
poco rit.
30
dim.
arco
pp sempre
poco rit.
88
40
Hb.
Hr. in E
Hr. in D
Trp. in D
Pk.
ben marc.

89
91
Fl.
Hb.
Kl.
Fg.
Hr. in E
Hr. in D
Trp. in D
Pk.
Solo-Vl.
Solo-Vcl.
Vl. I.
Vl. II.
Br.
Vcl.
B.
60
arco
p dim.
dim.
div.
90
50
pizz.
92
70
80
poco f
mf

93
Fg.
Hr. in D
Solo-Vl.
Solo-Vcl.
Vl. I.
Vl. II.
Br.
Vcl.
B.
pizz.
f arco
Fl.
Kl.
Fg.
Hr. in E
mf cresc.
mf
arco
95
100
Fl.
Hb.
Fg.
dol.
p dol.
Solo-Vl.
Solo-Vcl.
Vl. I
Vl. II
Br.
Vcl.
B.
arco
pp
arco div.
pizz.
p legg.
94
90
Fl.
Kl.
Fg.
Solo-Vl.
Solo-Vcl.
Vl. I.
Vl. II.
Br.
Vcl.
B.
pizz.
96
Hb.
Fg.
Solo-Vl.
Solo-Vcl.
Vl. I
Vl. II
Br.
Vcl.
arco
p legg.
110
Fl.
Hb.
Hr. in D
Trp. in D
Pk.
pp
legg.
dim.

97
Kl.
Fg.
Hr. in D
Trp. in D
Pk.
Solo-Vl.
Solo-Vcl.
Vl. I
Vl. II
Br.
Vcl.
B.
dim.
ff sempre
mf
arco
120
98
pizz.
130
99
Fl.
Hb.
Hr. in E
100
140

101
Fl.
Hb.
Kl.
Fg.
Hr. in D
Trp. in D
Solo-Vl.
Solo-Vcl.
Vl. I
Vl. II
Br.
Vcl
B.
pp dol.
pizz.
arco
p
pp
102
150
pp dol.
legg.
103
160
dim.
dim
f
170
104
180
p legg.
legg.
pp.

105
107
Hr. in D
Trp. in D
Solo-Vl.
Solo-Vcl.
Vl. I
Vl. II
Br.
Vcl.
B.
div.
Fl.
Hb.
Kl.
Fg.
ff
pp
106
190
Hr. in E
dim.
108
200

109
Fl.
Hb.
Kl.
Fg.
Hr. in E
Hr. in D
Trp. in D
Vl. I
Vl. II
Br.
Vcl.
B.
a 2
sf
111
Fl.
Hb.
Kl.
Fg.
Hr. in E
Hr. in D
Trp. in D
Pk.
Solo-Vl.
Solo-Vcl.
Vl. I
Vl. II
Br.
Vcl.
B.
a 2
fp
dim.
tr
ff
pizz.
p
110
210
Fl.
Hb.
Kl.
Fg.
Hr. in E
Hr. in D
Trp. in D
Pk.
Solo-Vl.
Solo-Vcl.
Vl. I
Vl. II
Br.
Vcl.
B.
sf
ff
112
220
Fl.
Hb.
Kl.
Fg.
Hr. in D
Pk.
Solo-Vcl.
Vl. I
Vl. II
Br.
Vcl.
B.
a 2
I.
p
arco

113
Fl.
Kl.
Fg.
Solo-Vl.
Solo-Vcl.
Vl.I
Vl.II
Br.
Vcl.
B.
230
Hr. in D
Pk.
114
Hb.
Hr. in E
legg.
115
240
dolce
legg.
116
molto leggiero e dolce
più p
div.
p dolce
arco
poco rit.
dim.
pp

117
250 in tempo
Kl.
Solo-Vl.
marc. e cresc. molto
Solo-Vcl.
marc. e cresc. molto
Vl.I
Vl.II
Br.
pizz.
Vcl.
pizz.
B.
Fl.
mf cresc.
Kl.
mf cresc.
Fg.
mf cresc.
Solo-Vl.
Solo-Vcl.
Br.
arco
Vcl.
119
Fl.
Hb.
Kl.
Fg.
Hr. in E
Hr. in D
Trp. in D
Pk.
Vl.I
Vl.II
Br.
Vcl.
B.
118
260
Fl.
Hb.
Kl.
Fg.
a 2
Hr. in E
Hr. in D
Trp. in D
Pk.
Solo-Vl.
Solo-Vcl.
Vl.I
Vl.II
Br.
Vcl.
B.
arco
120
Fl.
Hb.
Kl.
Fg.
a 2
Hr. in E
Hr. in D
Trp. in D
a 2
Pk.
Solo-Vl.
Solo-Vcl.
Vl.I
Vl.II
Br.
Vcl.
B.

Poco meno Allegro.
Hr. in E
Solo-Vl.
Solo-Vcl.
Vl.I
Vl.II
Br.
Vcl.
B.
Fg.
Fl.
Kl.
Trp. in D
Hb.
Hr. in D
dim.
mf dim.
p dolce
pizz.
arco
poco f
a 2
cresc.
p cresc.
div.
più p
pp
270
280
290
300
122
124

125
Hb.
Kl.
Fg.
Hr. in E
Hr. in D
Solo-Vl.
Solo-Vcl.
Vcl.
B.
I.
IV.
pizz.
310
Fl.
cresc.
126
dim.
arco
Vl. I
Br.
127
Vl. II
div.
128

129
131
130
132
320
330
Tempo primo.
Fl.
Hb.
Kl.
Fg.
Hr. in E
Hr. in D
Trp. in D
Solo-Vl.
Solo-Vcl.
Vl. I
Vl. II
Br.
Vcl.
B.
f marc.
p cresc.
cresc.

Fl.
Hb.
Kl.
Fg.
Hr. in E
Hr. in D
Trp. in D
Pk.
Solo-Vl.
Solo-Vcl.
Vl. I
Vl. II
Br.
Vcl.
B.

MAX BRUCH

CONCERTO in G minor, Op. 26 *Score P. 81*

Max Bruch made his first sketches for this concerto in 1857, but only worked seriously upon it in 1865 and 1866. The première, which took place on April 24, 1866, at Coblenz, had been postponed twice because of the illness of Johann Naret-Koning, concertmaster of the Mannheim Orchestra, whom Bruch had particularly desired to play it; at the last moment the soloist was Otto von Königslöw, concertmaster of the Gürzenich Orchestra in Cologne, with the composer conducting.

Bruch immediately set himself the task of revising the work, sending the new version to Joseph Joachim for critical advice; Joachim strenuously opposed Bruch's wish to call the work a fantasy rather than a concerto because of the free form of the first movement, writing him as follows: "I find that the title 'concerto' is fully justified; the last two movements are too completely and symmetrically developed for a fantasy. The different sections are brought together in beautiful relationship and yet—and this is the principal thing—there is sufficient contrast. Spohr, moreover, called his *Gesangsscene* a concerto."

Joachim, to whom Bruch finally dedicated the concerto, played the work in its revised form at Bremen on Jan. 7, 1868, and Sarasate gave the first American performance at a concert in New York in 1872. To many musical authorities it seems unfortunate that the popularity of this concerto has led to the neglect to a large extent of Bruch's other concertos Op. 4 and Op. 58; also of the *Concertstück,* Op. 84, the *Romance,* Op. 42 and of the *Scotch Fantasy,* Op. 46; all of these are serious works, deeply inspired and admirably adapted to the needs of the virtuoso.

Concerto No. 1 in G minor, Op. 26

4

6

7
Fl.
Hob.
Kl.
Fag.
Hór.
Tromp.
Pk.
pp
poco cresc.
Viol.
Br.
Vcl.
Ktb.
fp
sf
rfz

9
ritard.
Fl.
Hob.
Kl.
Fag.
Hór.
Tromp.
Pk.
cresc.
espress.
Viol.
Br.
Vcl.
Ktb.
pp

8
B
a tempo
colla parte
Fl.
Hob.
Kl.
Fag.
Hór.
Tromp.
Pk.
largamente
f espress.
ritard.
a tempo
Viol.
Br.
Vcl.
Ktb.
arco
ff

10
Solo.
Hob.
dimin.
a tempo
Fag.
Hór.
molto espress.
sempre
Viol.
Br.
Vcl.
Ktb.
dol. pp
pizz.
arco
Fag.
ritard.
Horn 3 4.
cresc.
mf

11
Un poco più lento.
Horn 3.4.
pp
molto espress.
ff
Viol.
pp
Br.
pp
poco cresc.
Vcl.
pp
poco cresc.
Ktb. pizz.
arco
poco cresc.
Hör.
espress.
rfz
2da
p molto cresc.
Viol.
pp
pp Br.
pp
Vcl.
pp Ktb.
pp
13
Fl.
Hob.
Kl.
Fag.
p
Hör.
cresc. poco
p
cresc. poco
Tromp.
Pk.
ff
rfz
Viol.
Br.
pizz.
arco
rfz
Vcl.
Ktb.
rfz
12
Kl.
colla parte
C Tempo I
Horn 1.2.
sfz
p
colla parte
pp
Pk.
ad libit.
pp
sfz
ff
Viol.
pp
p
trem.
colla parte
Br.
pp
pp trem.
Vcl.
pizz.
Ktb.
pp
colla parte
pizz.
pp
colla parte
Hör.
mf
mf
mf
Pk.
pp
Viol. trem.
pp
Br.
Vcl.
Ktb.
14
Fag.
pp
Horn 34.
pp
rfz
Viol.
pp
Br.
pp
Vcl.
rfz
Ktb.
rfz
dol.
Fl.
Fag.
Horn 1.2.
11
Viol.
Br.
Vcl.
Ktb.

string. poco a poco
15
17
16
18
Fl.
Fag.
Horn 3.4.
Pk.
Viol.
pizz.
Br.
Vcl. u. Ktb.
Hob.
Kl.
cresc.
sempre cresc.
arco
Hör.
Tromp.
Vcl.
Ktb.

19
Un poco più vivo.
Fl.
p cresc.
Hob.
Kl.
Fag.
Hör.
Tromp.
Pk.
Viol.
con fuoco
Br.
Vcl.
arco
Ktb.

D
21
Fl.
Hob.
Kl.
Fag.
Hör.
Tromp.
Pk.
Viol.
Br.
Vcl.
Ktb.

20
Fl.
Hob.
Kl.
Fag.
Hör.
Tromp.
Pk.
Viol.
Br.
Vcl.
Ktb.

22
Fl.
Hob.
Kl.
Fag.
Hör.
Tromp.
Pk.
Viol.
Br.
Vcl.
Ktb.

23
Fl.
Hob.
Kl.
Fag.
Hör.
Tromp.
Pk.
Viol.
Br.
Vcl.
Ktb.
sempre ff
marc.
sempre ff

24
E
Fl.
Hob.
Kl.
Fag.
Hör.
Tromp.
Pk.
Viol.
Br.
Vcl.
Ktb.

25
poco ritard.
Tempo I.
(Allº mod.)
Fl.
Hob.
Kl.
Fag.
Hör.
Tromp.
Pk.
muta in B. Es.
p decresc.
Viol.
Br.
Vcl.
Ktb.
decresc.
pp

26
Fl.
Kl.
Fag.
Horn 1.2.
Solo
ad libit.
string.
Hob.
Hör.
p cresc.
a tempo
ff ad libit.

Solo.
a tempo (Allegro.)
string.
Allegro moderato.
F
Fl.
Hob.
Kl.
Fag.
Hör.
Tromp.
in Es.
Pk.
in Es.B.
Viol.
Br.
Vcl.
Ktb.

Fl.
Hob.
Kl.
Fag.
Hör.
Tromp.
Pk.
Viol.
morendo
attacca
Br.
Vcl.
Ktb.

Fl.
Hob.
Kl.
Fag.
Hör.
Tromp.
Pk.
Viol.
Br.
Vcl.
Ktb.

II. Adagio.

Adagio.
2 Flöten.
2 Hoboen.
2 Klarinetten in B.
2 Fagotte.
2 Hörner in Es (I.II.)
2 Hörner in B (III.IV.)
2 Trompeten in Es.
Pauken in Es.B.
3: a corda
espress.
cresc.
Solo-Violine.
Violine I.
Violine II.
Bratsche.
Violoncell.
Kontrabass.

Horn 1.2.
A
4ta corda
Viol.
Br.
Vcl.
Ktb.
pizz.
div.
arco
cresc.
32
B
Fl.
Fag.
dolce
poco ritard. a tempo
Hob.
Fg.
C
p cresc.
34
Kl.
Hör.
Tromp.
Pk.

35
Fag.
Hör.
Viol.
f sostenuto
Br.
Vcl.
cresc.
Ktb.
arco
D
Pk.
f pesante
pizz.
37
Fl.
Hob.
Kl.
Fag.
Hör.
Tromp.
Pk.
tranquillo
Viol.
Br.
pizz.
Vcl.
Ktb.
36
Fl.
Hob.
Kl.
Fag.
Hör.
Tromp.
Pk.
pesante
Viol.
Br.
arco
Vcl.
sempre p
Ktb.
38
Fl.
Hob.
Kl.
Fag.
Hör.
Tromp.
Pk.
cresc.
Viol.
Br.
Vcl.
pizz.
Ktb.

39
Fl.
Hob.
Kl.
Fag.
Hör.
sempre p
Tromp.
Pk.
E
4ta corda
Viol.
Br.
arco
Vcl.
Ktb.

41
a tempo
F
a2.
Kl.
Fag.
p cresc.
Horn 1.
Pk.
Viol.
div.
cresc.
Br.
Vcl.
Ktb.
molto espress.
2da
pizz.
arco

40
Hör.
Pk.
Viol.
Br.
Vcl.
pizz.
Ktb.
Kl.
Fag.
Horn 3.
cresc.
ritard.
dol.
poco cresc.
sempre cresc.

42
3ta
mf espress.
cresc.
G
2da
Viol. arco
sempre pp
Br.
Vcl. arco
espress.
Ktb. arco
pizz.
Kl.
Fag.
Viol.
Br.
Vcl.
Ktb.

Fl.
Hob.
Kl.
Fag.
Hör.
Tromp.
Pk.
Viol.
Br.
Vcl.
Ktb.
arco
cresc.
f cresc.

H
Fl.
Hob.
Kl.
Fag.
Hör.
Tromp.
Pk.
Viol.
Br.
Vcl.
Ktb.

a 2.
Fl.
Hob.
Kl.
Fag.
Hör.
Tromp.
Pk.
Viol.
Br.
Vcl.
Ktb.
rfz
sempre cresc.
cresc.
sfz

Fl.
Hob.
Kl.
Fag.
Hör.
Tromp.
Pk.
Viol.
Br.
Vcl.
Ktb.

47

Fl. p

Hob.

Kl. p

Fag.

Hör.

Tromp.

Pk.

Viol. pp

pp

Br.

Vcl. pizz.

Ktb. pizz.

49

Fl. Solo espress.

Hob.

Kl.

Fag.

Hör. p pp

Tromp. pp

Pk. pp

Viol. pp pp

Br. pp

Vcl. pp pp

Ktb. p pp pizz.

48

Fl.

Kl.

Fag.

Hör. p

tranquillo

6 6 6

Viol.

Br. p

Vcl.

Ktb.

Kl. p

Hör.

6 6 cresc.

f

Viol. p

p

Br. p

Vcl. div. p

Ktb. arco arco

50

I Fl.

Horn 1. Solo espress.

Tromp.

Pk. pp

4ta corda cresc.

Viol.

Br.

Vcl.

Ktb.

Horn 1.

Viol. p pp

Br. pp

Vcl. pp

Ktb.

51
K
L
Fag.
Horn 1.2.
Viol.
Br.
Vcl.
Ktb.
Fl.
Kl.
Pk.
espr.
cresc.
poco cresc.
div.
arco
pizz.
molto cresc.
sfz
morendo
ppp

Fl.
Hob.
Kl.
a 2.
Fag.
Hör.
Tromp.
Pk.
Viol.
Br.
Vcl.
Ktb.
cresc.
p cresc.

III. Finale.

Allegro energico.
2 Flöten.
2 Hoboen.
2 Klarinetten in B.
2 Fagotte.
2 Hörner in D.
2 Hörner in C.
2 Trompeten in D
Pauken in G.D.
Solo-Violine.
Violine I.
Violine II.
Bratsche.
Violoncell.
Kontrabass.

A
Fl.
Hob. a 2.
Kl.
Fag. a 2.
Hör.
Tromp.
cresc.
Pk.
Viol.
Br.
Vcl.
Ktb.
pizz.
ff

55
Fag.
Horn 1.2.
Viol.
Br.
Vcl.
Ktb.
57
Fl.
Hob.
Kl.
Fag.
Hör.
Tromp.
Pk.
pizz.
56
B.
58
au talon
arco

59
Fl.
Hob.
Kl.
Fag.
Hör.
Tromp.
Pk.
au talon
Viol.
pizz.
arco
Br.
Vcl.
Ktb.

61
Fl.
Hob.
Kl.
Fag.
Hör.
a 2.
Tromp.
Pk.
Viol.
Br.
Vcl.
Ktb.

60
C
Fl.
cresc.
Hob.
Kl.
Fag.
Hör.
a 2.
Tromp.
Pk.
Viol.
Br.
Vcl.
arco
Ktb.

62
Fl.
a 2.
Hob.
Kl.
Fag.
Hör.
Tromp.
Pk.
Viol.
Br.
Vcl.
Ktb.

63

D
Fl.
Hob.
Kl.
a 2.
Fag.
a 2.
Hör.
sf
sf
Tromp.
Pk.
sf
Viol.
sf
Br.
Vcl.
Ktb.
sf

64

Kl.
Fag.
p
Horn 1.2.
p
fp
fp
f
Viol.
pizz.
Br.
pizz.
p
Vcl.
pizz.
Ktb.
pizz.
p
sf
Kl.
p
Fag.
Horn 1.2.
non ligato
cresc.
f
Viol.
p
sf
Br.
Vcl.
Ktb.

65

Kl.
Fag.
cresc.
Viol.
Br.
Vcl.
Ktb.
Kl.
Fag.
Horn 1.2.
p
f
f
f
f
Viol.
sf
Br.
Vcl.
Ktb.

66

Kl
Horn 1.2.
pp
p
con fuoco
f
Viol.
pp
arco
Br.
pp
Vcl.
arco
pp
Ktb.
arco
pp
Ob.
p
Kl.
cresc.
p
Fag.
cresc.
Horn 1.
p
Viol
p
cresc.
p
cresc.
Br.
p
cresc.
Vcl.
p
cresc.
Ktb.
p
cresc.

E
Fl.
Hob.
Kl.
Fag.
Hör.
Tromp.
Pk.
Viol.
Br.
Vcl.
Ktb.
a 2
ff
molto cresc.
sempre
ff marcato
ff trem.
marcato

Fl.
Hob.
Kl.
Fag.
Hör.
Tromp.
Pk.
Viol.
Br.
Vcl.
Ktb.
ff
sf
a 2

Fl.
Hob.
Kl.
Fag.
Hör.
Tromp.
Pk.
4ta Corda
f
con forza
Viol.
Br.
Vcl.
Ktb.
p trem.
pp
pizz.
p

Fag.
Horn 1.2.
4ta Corda
Viol.
Br.
Vcl.
Ktb.
arco
Hob.
Kl.
Fag.
Hör.
cresc.
pp
mf
fp
sf
a 2

71

Hob.
Kl.
Fag.
grazioso
cresc.
Viol.
p dolce
Br.
Vcl.
Ktb.
pizz.
poco rit.
arco

72

a tempo
tranquillo
Viol.
Br.
Vcl.
Ktb.
Kl.
Fag.
Horn 1.2.
p dolce
cresc. e string.

73

Kl.
Fag.
Horn 1.2.
decresc.
Viol.
Br.
Vcl.
Ktb.
Hob.
con forza

74

F
Fl.
Hob.
Kl.
Fag.
Hörn
Tromp.
Pk.
a 2
Viol.
Br.
Vcl.
Ktb

75

Fl.
Hob.
a 2
Kl.
Fag.
rfz
Hör.
a 2
ff
Tromp.
a 2
Pk.
Viol.
Br.
rfz
Vcl.
rfz
Ktb.
rfz

77

Fl.
ff
Hob.
a 2
ff
Kl.
ff
Fag.
ff
Hör. a 2
ff
a 2
ff
Tromp.
ff
Pk.
ff
10
Viol.
ff
ff
Br.
ff
Vcl.
ff
rf
rf
rf
Ktb.
ff
rf
rf
rf

76

Fl.
a 2
Hob.
Kl.
Fag.
Hör.
Tromp.
Pk.
Viol.
Br.
rfz
Vcl.
rfz
Ktb
rfz

78

G
Fag.
p
Horn 1.2.
p
Viol.
pizz.
mf
pizz.
mf
Br. pizz.
mf
Vcl. pizz.
mf
Ktb. pizz.
mf
Kl.
p
Fag.
Horn 1.2.
p
au talon
ff
ff
Viol.
Br.
arco
p
Vcl.
Ktb.

Kl.
Horn 1.2.
sempre ff
rf
Viol.
legg.
legg.
pizz.
Br.
Vcl.
Ktb.
Fl.
Hob.
Kl.
Fag.
Horn 1.2.
rf
Viol.
Br.
arco
Vcl.
Ktb.

H
a 2
Fl.
Hob.
Kl.
cresc.
Fag.
cresc.
molto cresc.
Hör.
cresc.
molto cresc.
Tromp.
Pk.
Viol.
arco
cresc.
con forza
Br.
Vcl. arco
Ktb. arco
con forza

80

Fl.
Fag.
Horn 3.4.
Viol.
Br.
pizz.
arco
Vcl.
Ktb.
Fag.
Horn 3.4.
Viol.
arco
Br.
Vcl.
Ktb.

82

Fl.
Hob.
Kl.
Fag.
rfz
Hör.
rf
Tromp.
a 2
Pk.
Viol.
rfz
Br.
Vcl.
mf
Ktb.

Fl.
Hob.
Kl.
Fag.
Hör.
Tromp.
Pk.
Viol.
Br.
Vcl.
Ktb.
cresc.
marc.
p dolce

Fl.
Hob.
Kl.
Fag.
Hör.
Tromp.
Pk.
Viol.
Br.
Vcl.
Ktb.
cresc.
espressivo
tranquillo

Fag.
Horn 1.2.
espress.
Viol.
Br.
Vcl.
Ktb.
Kl.
divisi

Fl.
Hob.
Kl.
Fag.
Hör.
Tromp.
Pk.
Viol.
Br.
Vcl.
Ktb.
pizz.
cresc.
stringendo

88
Kl.
Fag.
Horn 1.2.
Viol.
Br.
Vcl.
Ktb.
pp
arco

90
Fl.
Hob.
Kl.
Fag.
Hör.
Tromp.
Pk.
Viol.
Br.
Vcl.
Ktb.
cresc.
arco

91

K
a 2
Fl.
Hob.
Kl.
Fag.
Hör.
Tromp.
Pk.
Viol.
con fuoco
Br.
Vcl.
Ktb.
K

92

Fl.
Hob.
Kl.
p cresc.
Fag.
Hör.
cresc.
Tromp.
Pk.
con fuoco
Viol.
p legg.
p legg.
Br.
Vcl.
Ktb.

Fl.
Hob.
Kl.
Fag.
Hör.
a 2
Tromp.
Pk.
Viol.
Br.
Vcl.
Ktb.

94

L
stringendo poco a poco
Fl.
Hob.
Fag.
Horn 1. 2.
stringendo
Viol.
Br.
Vcl.
Ktb.
Fl.
Hör.
un poco marc.
rf
Viol.
pp
Br.
Vcl.
Ktb.

95

Fl.
Hob.
Kl.
Fag.
Hör.
Tromp.
Pk.

ff appassionato
Viol.
pizz.
Br.
Vcl.
Ktb.

7

Presto.
Fl.
Hob.
Kl.
Fag.
Hör.
Tromp.
Pk.
con forza
Viol.
arco
pizz.
Br.
Vcl.
Ktb.

96

Fl.
Hob.
Kl.
Fag.
Hör.
Tromp.
Pk.
Viol.
Br.
Vcl.
Ktb.
cresc.

98

Fl.
Hob.
Kl.
Fag.
Hör.
Tromp.
a 2
Pk.
Viol.
arco
Br.
Vcl.
Ktb.

ANTONÍN DVOŘÁK

CONCERTO in A minor, Op. 53 *Score P. 106*

An unusually small amount of authentic, detailed information is available regarding the conception and composition of this work. During the early part of 1879, Dvořák was a guest at the home of the Prince de Rohan at the castle of Sychrov near Turnov in Bohemia; his thoughts turned to his intimate friend, Joseph Joachim, and this concerto was the result. Finished in May or June, 1879, Dvořák dispatched the work to Joachim for criticism and suggestions regarding the technical problems of the solo part.

The reasons for the delay between composition and première are not known, but three years elapsed before the first performance took place at Leipzig with Joachim as soloist. Franz Ondřiček played it first in Bohemia during 1883; years later both Jan Kubelik and Jaroslav Kocian introduced it successfully to audiences in both Europe and America.

The consensus of critical opinion does not place this work among the most important of its kind, or as one of Dvořák's most inspired creations, but there is no doubt that, with the increasing demand for new-old works upon the part of radio audiences, the concerto will continue to be heard more and more; it is charmingly conceived from the melodic standpoint, well developed from the point of construction and fully entitled to be classed among the masterpieces in its particular field.

Concerto in A minor, Op. 53

Antonín Dvořák

in tempo
5
30
Fl.
Hb.
Kl.
Fg.
(F)
Hr.
(D)
Tr.
(E)
zu 2
Solo
Vl.
Br.
Vc.
u. Kb.
7
pizz.
arco
dim.
50
Kb.
6
40
8
3. 4.
Pk.
A-D

9

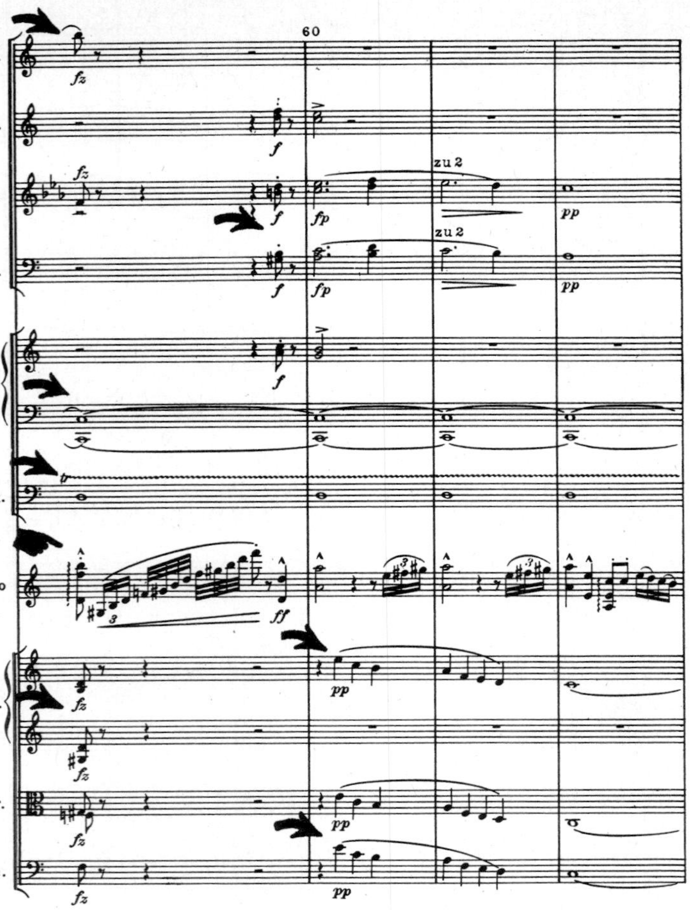
60
Fl.
Hb.
Kl.
Fg.
(F)
Hr.
(D)
Pk.
Solo
Vl.
Br.
Vc.
fz
f
fp
pp
ff
zu 2
tr

10

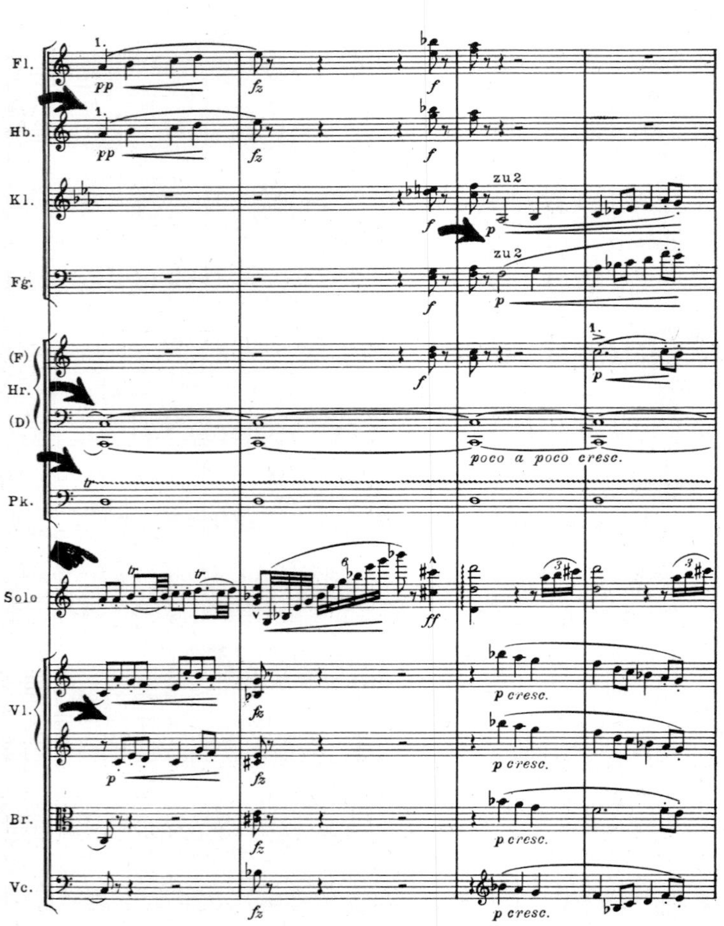
Fl.
Hb.
Kl.
Fg.
(F)
Hr.
(D)
Pk.
Solo
Vl.
Br.
Vc.
1.
pp
fz
f
p
ff
zu 2
poco a poco cresc.
p cresc.
tr

11

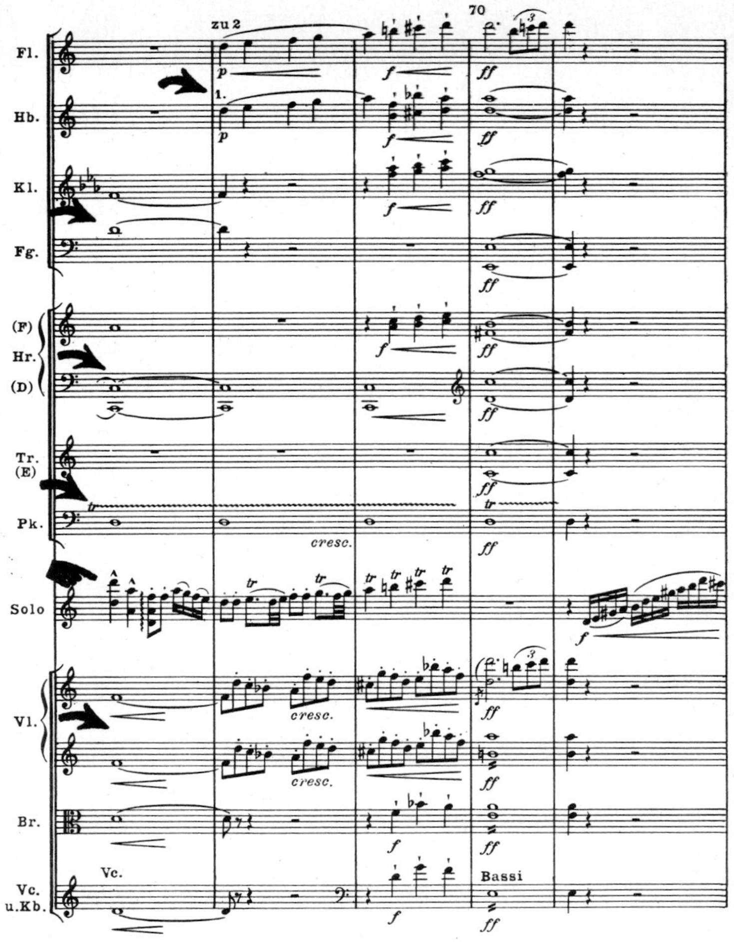
70
zu 2
Fl.
Hb.
Kl.
Fg.
(F)
Hr.
(D)
Tr.
(E)
Pk.
Solo
Vl.
Br.
Vc.
u. Kb.
1.
p
f
ff
cresc.
Vc.
Bassi
tr

12

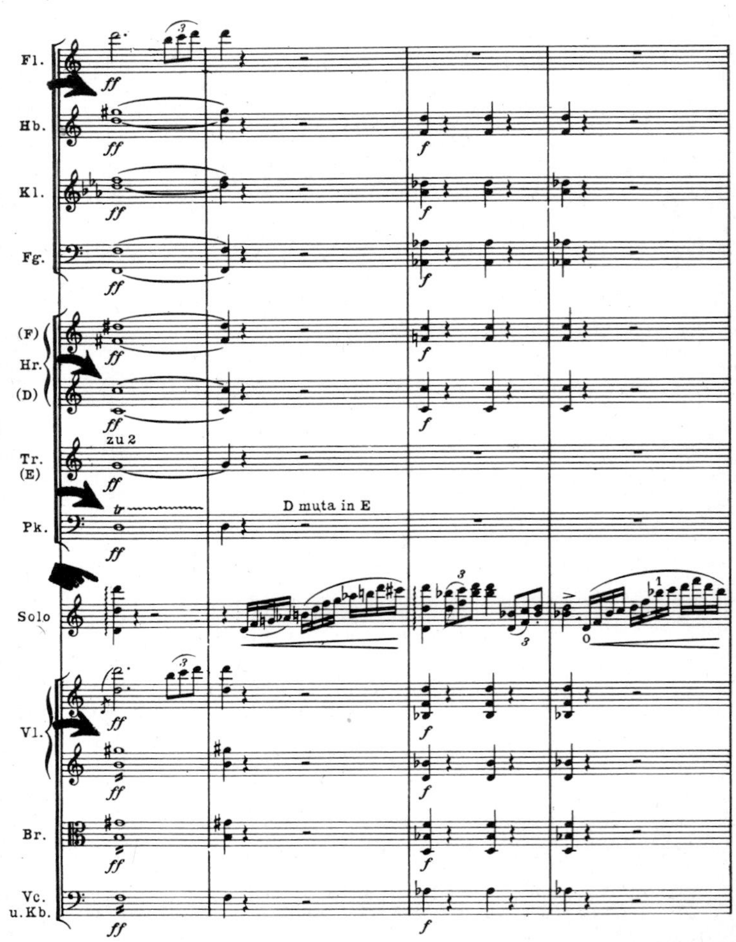
Fl.
Hb.
Kl.
Fg.
(F)
Hr.
(D)
Tr.
(E)
Pk.
Solo
Vl.
Br.
Vc.
u. Kb.
ff
f
zu 2
D muta in E
tr

13
80
Hb.
Kl.
Fg.
(F) Hr. (D)
Solo
Vl.
Br.
Vc. u. Kb.
p dolce
Bassi
mit immer breiterem Strich
100
15
cresc.
espressivo
pizz.
A-E
Pk.
14
90
zu 2
dim.
arco
16
110
Vc.
Kb.

17
Fl.
Hb.
Fg.
(F)
Hr.
(D)
Solo
Vl.
Br.
Vc.
Kb.
pizz.
18
cresc.
Vc.
u. Kb.
Bassi
arco
3. 4.
19
130
dolce e dimin.
20
140
Kl.
sempre più p
dim.
dolce
1. 2.

21
23
22
24
150
160
170
Fl.
Hb.
Kl.
Fg.
(F)
Hr.
(D)
Solo
Vl. II.
Vl.
Br.
Vc.
Kb.
zu 2
cresc.
dim.
scherzando
pizz.
arco
pp
p
mf
f
fz

Hb.
Kl.
Hr. (F)
Solo
Br.
Vc.
Kb.
fp
f
pp
fz
1.
Fl.
180
1. 2. zu 2
Vl. I.
pizz.
26
Hr. (D)
3. 4.
arco
Vl.
Bassi
190
tr
cresc.
28
ff rinforzando
pp sempre
Vc. u. Kb.
mf

29
31
30
32
210
zu 2
Fl.
Hb.
Kl.
Fg.
(F)
Hr.
(D)
Tr.
(E)
Pk.
Solo
Vl.
Br.
Vc.
Kb.
Vc.
u. Kb.
Bassi

33

Fl.
Hb.
Kl.
Fg.
(F) Hr. (D)
Tr. (E)
Pk.
Solo
Vl.
Br.
Vc. u. Kb.

Hb.
Kl.
Fg.
1.2.
Hr. (F)
Tr. (E)
Pk.
Solo
ff grandioso
Vl.
Br.
Vc. u. Kb.
Bassi

34

zu 2
220

Fl.
Hb.
Kl.
Fg.
(F) Hr. (D)
Tr. (E)
Pk.
Solo
Vl.
Br.
Vc.
Kb.

36

Solo
Vl.
Br.
Vc. u. Kb.

Solo
Vl.
Br.
Vc. u. Kb.

Hb.
Kl.
1.
Fg.
1.2. zu 2
Hr. (F)
Solo
Vl.
Br.
Vc. u. Kb.

37
Hb.
Kl.
Fg.
Hr. (F)
Solo
Vl.
Br.
Vc. u. Kb.
cresc.
240
38
Fl.
zu 2
Poco
Tr. (E)
muta in C
Pk.
meno mosso
250
39
3.4.
Hr. (D)
fp dimin. pp
dim.
Quasi moderato
molto espressivo
260
ritard.
muta in D
dimin.
muta in F
pespressivo
attacca
40
II
Adagio ma non troppo
pespress.
(in B)
cresc.
get.

20

Fl. Hb. Kl. Solo Br. Vc.

pp *dim.* *pp* *fp*

Fl. Hb. Kl. Hr. (F) Solo Vl. Br. Vc.

pp *p* *mf* *fp* *f* pizz. *fz*

42

30

Fl. Hb. Kl. Fg. Hr. (F) Solo Vl. Br. Vc.

pp *fp* *p* *fz* *cresc.* *dim.* pizz. Kb. pizz.

Fl. Hb. Kl. Fg. Solo Vl. Br. Vc. u. Kb.

dim. *pp* *f* *dim.* *p* arco

zu 2

40

Poco più mosso

Fl. Hb. Kl. Fg. Hr. (F) Solo Vl. Br. Vc. Kb.

f *dim.* *fz* *mf* *f pesante* arco *pp* *fp*

44

Fg. Hr. (F) Solo Vl. II Br. Vc. u. Kb.

p *f* *cresc.* *fz dim.* *pp* *dim.* Bassi

poco rit.

Hb. Kl. Fg. Hr. (F) Solo Vl. II Br. Vc. Kb.

p *pp* *fp* *dim.* pizz.

Tempo I
45
Più mosso
arco
Un poco tranquillo, quasi Tempo I
47
46
48
Bassi
Kl.
Fg.
Hr. (F)
Solo
Br.
Vc.
Kb.
Hb.
Vl.
Vl.II
Vc. u.Kb.
Fl.
cresc.
dim.

49
50
51
52
90
100
110
in tempo
poco accelerando
stringendo
poco ritard.
in tempo
poco stringendo
pizz.
arco
zu 2
dim.
pesante
Bassi
Hb.
Fg.
Hr. (F)
Solo
Vl.
Br.
Vc.
Kb.
Fl.
Kl.
Tr. (C)
Vc. u. Kb.

53
rit.
in tempo
Hb.
Kl.
Fg.
Hr. (F)
Tr. (C)
Br.
Vc.
Kb.
dim.
55
Fl.
Solo
Vl.
pizz.
54
120
muta in E
56
130
pp dim.
p espressivo
arco

57
1.
Hb.
Fg.
Hr. (F)
Solo
Vl.
Br.
Vc.
Kb.
p
pp
f
Fl.
Kl.
dim.
59
zu 2
150
ff
58
140
p molto cresc.
f pesante
Bassi
Vc. u. Kb.
60
2.
1.
4.
dolce

61
63
62
64
III. Finale
Allegro giocoso, ma non troppo
2 Flöten
2 Hoboen
2 Klarinetten in A
2 Fagotte
2 Hörner in E
2 Hörner in D
2 Trompeten in E
Pauken in A-E
Solo-Violine
Violine I
Violine II
Bratsche
Violoncell Kontrabaß
rit.
in tempo
morendo
2da corda
Bassi
pizz.
arco

65

Hr. (D)
Solo
Vl.
Br.
Vc.
pizz.
Vc. pizz.
Fl.
Hb.
Kl.
Fg.
Hr. (E)
zu 2
arco
Vc. u. Kb.
Bassi

66

Fl.
Hb.
Kl.
Fg.
Hr. (E)
Tr. (E)
Pk.
Solo
Vl.
Br.
Vc. u. Kb.
cresc.
zu 2
pizz.

67

Fl.
Hb.
Kl.
Fg.
(E) Hr. (D)
zu 2
Tr. (E)
Pk.
Solo
Vl.
Br.
arco
Vc. u. Kb.

68

Fl.
Hb.
Kl.
Fg.
(E)
Hr.
(D)
Tr.
(E)
Pk.
Solo
Vl.
Br.
Vc.
u.Kb.
pp
p
mf
f
1.
zu 2
tr
ff
get.
pizz.
arco
Vc.
Bassi

80
Hb.
Kl.
Fg.
(E)
Hr.
(D)
Tr.
(E)
Pk.
Vl.
Br.
Vc.
u.Kb.
fz
f
zu 2
3

70

70
Hb.
Kl.
Fg.
(E)
Hr.
(D)
Tr.
(E)
Pk.
Vl.
Br.
Vc.
u.Kb.
f
fz
1.
tr

72

90
Hb.
Kl.
Fg.
(E)
Hr.
(D)
Tr.
(E)
Pk.
Vl.
Br.
Vc.
u.Kb.
zu 2
f
3

73
75
74
76
Hb.
Kl.
Fg.
(E)
Hr.
(D)
Tr.
(E)
Pk.
Vl.
Br.
Vc.
u.Kb.
Kb.
Fl.
Solo
Vl.II
zu 2
A muta in H
staccato sempre
spiccato
pizz.
pp Bassi
dim.
100
110
120
130
140
150

77
78
79
80
Fl.
Hb.
Kl.
Fg.
Hr.
(E)
(D)
Tr.
Pk.
Solo
Vl.
Br.
Vc.
u.Kb.
Kb.
zu 2
H muta in A
arco
pizz.
dolce
dimin.
cresc.
poco a poco
160
170
180
190
200
210

81
220
Fl.
Hb.
cresc.
Kl.
Fg.
p cresc.
1.2.
Hr.
(E)
Solo
f
fz
Vl.
arco
Br.
pp
Vc.
Kb.
83
1.
250
zu 2
Hr.
(D)
Tr.
(E)
Pk.
Vc.
u.Kb.
82
230
Bassi
240
ff
84
4.
260
cresc.

85
270
Hb.
Kl.
Fg.
Hr. (E)
Solo
Vl.
Br.
Vc. u.Kb.
cresc.
1.2.
280
Tr. (E)
Pk.
86
Fl.
zu 2
Hr.
(E)
(D)
fp
non legato
fpp
Vc.
Kb.
87
290
300
3.4.
Hr. (D)
pp
mf
segue
fz
pizz.
88
1.
arco

89
91
Fl.
Hb.
Kl.
Fg.
(E) Hr. (D)
Tr. (E)
Pk.
E muta in D
Vl.
Br.
Vc.
Kb.
Vc. u.Kb.
p dimin.
dimin.
pizz.
pp
90
Solo
arco
Bassi
92
L'istesso tempo
(Ein 2/4 Takt gleich zwei früheren 3/8 Takten)
mf molto espressivo
310
320
330
340
350
360
370

93
95
94
96
380
390
400
410
420
Hb.
Kl.
Fg.
Solo
Vl.
Br.
Vc. u. Kb.
Vc.
Kb.
(E) Hr. (D)
Pk.
zu 2
dim.
4. corda
ff pesante
pp Bassi
pizz.
arco
cresc.
4ª corda
D≥A

Fl.
Hb.
Fg.
Solo
Vc. u. Kb.
poco a poco cresc.
430
cresc.
Hr. (D)
Pk.
D muta in E
98
Vl.
Br.
440
Tempo I
Kl.
(E) Hr. (D)
Tr. (E)
E-A.
4ta corda
pizz.
450
get.
sempre pp
arco
460
zu 2
100
470

101

Fl. Hb. Kl. Fg. (E) Hr. (D) Tr. (E) Pk. Solo Vl. Br. Vc. u. Kb.

3.4. 1. pizz. Vc pizz. pizz.

ff fp pp f p

Kl. Fg. Solo Vl. Br. Vc.

480 1.

102

490

Fl. Hb. Kl. Fg. (E) Hr. (D) Tr. (E) Pk. Solo Vl. Br. Vc. Kb.

zu 2 zu 2 arco arco arco

f fz

103

Hb. Kl. Fg. (E) Hr. (D) Tr. (E) Vl. Br. Vc. Kb.

zu 2 1.

p fz f

104

500

Hb. Kl. Fg. (E) Hr. (D) Tr. (E) Pk. Vl. Br. Vc. u. Kb.

zu 2 Bassi

f

510
Hb.
Kl.
Fg.
1. 2.
Hr. (E)
zu 2
Tr. (E)
Pk.
Vl.
Br.
Vc. u. Kb.
fz

Solo
p
stacc. sempre
Vl.
Br.
Vc.
Kb.

540
Fg.
2.
p
Hr. (E)
1.
Solo
fz
Vl.
pp
Br.
pizz.
Vc.
Kb.

106

520
Hb.
Kl.
Fg.
Hr. (E)
1. 2.
Tr. (E)
Vl.
Br.
Vc. u. Kb.
fz
f
dim.
530
p
pp

108

550
Hb.
2.
p
Kl.
Fg.
1.
Hr. (D)
3. 4.
Solo
fz
Vl.
pp
Br.
Vc.
Kb.

109
560
Hb.
Kl.
Fg.
(E)
Hr.
(D)
Pk.
Solo
Vl.
Br.
Vc. u. Kb.
Bassi
570
zu 2
110
580
arco
111
590
Tr. (E)
poco marcato
600
cresc.
112
Fl.

113
115
114
116
Fl.
Hb.
Kl.
Fg.
(E) Hr. (D)
Tr. (E)
Pk.
Solo
Vl.
Br.
Vc.
Kb.
Hr. (E)
Vc. u. Kb.
zu 2
f molto espr.
dim.
cresc.
pizz.
arco
Bassi
poco a poco cresc.

117

Fl. Hb. Kl. Fg. Hr. (E) Tr. (E) Pk. Solo Vl. Br. Vc. u. Kb.

f p cresc. fz

119

680

Fl. Hb. Kl. Fg. (E) Hr. (D) Tr. (E) Pk. Solo Vl. Br. Vc. u. Kb.

f tr

118

670

Fl. Hb. Kl. Fg. Hr. (E) Tr. (E) Pk. Solo Vl. Br. Vc. u. Kb.

f tr ff

120

690

Fg. Solo Vl. I.

fp dimin. p pp

Fg. Hr. (E) Solo Vl. I.

fp pp dimin. 1. 2. dimin. pp

700 poco marcato

Fl. Fg. Hr. (E) Solo Vl. Br. Vc.

1. p pp leggiero ppp

121
123
L'istesso tempo
Fl.
Solo
Vl.
Br.
Vc.
Hb.
Kl.
Fg.
Hr.
Tr.
Pk.
Vc. u. Kb.
Bassi
restez
sempre stacc. e pp
cresc.
122
124
zu 2
Kb.

125
Tempo I
Hb.
Kl.
Fg.
(E) Hr. (D)
Tr. (E)
Pk.
Solo
dimin.
Vl.
Br.
Vc.
Kb.
760
cresc.
126
770
Fl.
fz
780
1. 2.
127
Bassi
Vc. u. Kb.
790
128
zu 2
800

poco accelerando
Fl.
Hb.
Kl.
Fg.
pp
cresc.
(E)
Hr.
(D)
Tr.
(E)
Pk.
ppp
Solo
ff
Vl.
Br.
Vc.
Kb.
130
810
zu 2
f

ALEXANDER GLAZOUNOFF

CONCERTO in A minor, Op. 82 *Score P. 140*

It is extremely unfortunate that little information of detailed character is available regarding the lives and major works of many eminent Russian composers—among them, Alexander Glazounoff; it would indeed be a boon if the wealth of data available regarding Tschaikowsky and Rimsky-Korsakoff could also be found about Glazounoff, Glière, Borodin, Shostakovich and a score more Russians whose works are frequently heard today in both concert and broadcast.

The known facts regarding this concerto are exceedingly few. It was conceived in 1904 and completed in 1905; the composer dedicated it to Leopold Auer who performed it for the first time at a concert of the Imperial Musical Society in St. Petersburg during the 1904-1905 season.

Glazounoff, whose activities were chiefly in the field of instrumental music, was presumably allied with the "Russian School" of Balakireff, Rimsky-Korsakoff and Moussorgsky, but he differed from them in preferring the classic form; and displays an understanding and mastery of it to an unusual degree in this concerto; M. Montagu-Nathan, in his *History of Russian Music,* says of it: "Though it eschews formalistic severity, the concerto is classical as to thematic material, development and harmonization."

Concerto in A minor, Op. 82
Alexander Glazounoff
Moderato M. M. ♩=92
1 Flauto piccolo (poi Fl. III)
2 Flauti grandi
2 Oboi
2 Clarinetti
in B
2 Fagotti
4 Corni in F
2 Trombe
3 Tromboni (poi)
Timpani
Campanelli (poi)
Triangolo
Piatti
Arpa (poi)
Violino solo
dolce espressivo
Violini I
Violini II
Viole
Violoncelli
Contrabassi
pizz.
3
4
5
6
espress.
animato ♩=112
Ossia
etc.
Vcl. arco
arco
Bassi e Vcl.
calando
riten.
a tempo
Vcl. e Bassi
Fl. gr.
Ob.
Cl.
Fag.
Cor. (F)
Solo
Viol.
Vle.
Vcl.
Cb.
Vcl. e Cb.

7
Fl. gr.
Ob.
Cl.
Fag.
Cor. (F)
Solo
Viol.
Vle.
Vcl.
Cb.
espress.
pizz.
tranquillo
a piacere
dolce
espr.
8
animando
rallent.
a tempo
arco
9
animando
calando
cresc. poco
cresc.
dim.
cres.
riten.
a tempo
dolce espress.
div. espress.
10
Più mosso ♩=120
pp cresc.

Fl. gr.
Ob.
Cl.
Fag.
Cor. (F)
Solo
Viol.
Vle.
Vcl.
Cb.
Timp.
Trg!.
Vcl. e Cb.
12
Fl. p.
Tbe. (B)
Trgl.
pizz.
arco
(pizz)
(Tempo I)
14
calando
unis.
espress.
div. arco
cresc.
dim.
poco

15
rallent.
Tranquillo 𝅗𝅥=76
Fl. p.
Fl. gr.
Solo
II.
Ob.
Cl.
Solo
Fag.
Solo
Viol.
div.
Vle.
unis.
Vcl.
Cb.
17
Andante sostenuto 𝅗𝅥=56
Fag.
I.
Arpa
sul G dolce espress.
Solo
Vle.
I. II.
III. IV.
Vcl.
Cl.
Fag.
Arpa
Solo
espress.
Vle.
espress.
I. II. unis.
pizz.
Vcl.
2 Cb. pizz.
Cb.
16
riten.
Fl. gr.
I.
Ob.
Cl.
I.
Fag.
Arpa
Solo
Viol.
dim.
div.
Vle.
dim.
div. a 3
Vcl.
dim.
Cb.
18
II.
Fl. gr.
I.
Cl.
Fag.
I.
Cor. (F)
cresc.
Arpa
cresc.
passionato
Solo
cresc.
Vle.
cresc.
div.
arco
Vcl.
Tutti div.
arco
Cb.
II. pizz.

19
Fl. gr.
Ob.
I
I. Solo
Cl.
Fag.
Cor. (F)
Arpa
Solo
Viol.
Vle.
sul D
Vcl.
pizz.
Tutti pizz.
Cb.
21
I. Solo
I. in B
II. in A
p espress.
più piano
div.
div. arco
pizz.
II. arco
div. I. arco
II. pizz.
20
cresc.
III.
p cresc.
22
agitato
II. in A
unis.

23
Ob.
I.
mp
f
Cl.
II.
in B
Cor. (F)
Arpa
muta C Dis Es Fis Ges A His
Solo
espress.
Viol.
mf
Vle.
Vcl.
Cb.
24
Fl. gr.
Fag.
gliss.
unis. arco
Vcl. e Cb.
dim.
div.
calando
III.
p
II. pizz.
25
unis. arco
a tempo
in B
26
pizz.
cresc.
(la ♮)
pp

27
29
28
30
Fl. gr.
Ob.
Cl.
Fag.
Cor. (F)
Tbe. (B)
Arpa
Solo
Viol.
Vle.
Vcl.
Cb.
Fl.
(in B)
più piano
pizz.
arco
div.
unis.
dim.
(la ♮)

31
Tempo I
riten.
Fag.
Cor. (F)
Viol.
Vle.
Vcl.
a tempo
riten.
Fl.
Ob.
Cl.
div.
pizz.
32
a tempo
riten. poco
Fl. gr.
sul A
unis.
33
riten. poco
a tempo. Più animato ♩=112
in A
Solo
arco
pizz.
34
Viol. II
(pizz.)
Tbe. (A)
in A
p espress.

pesante
35
37
Fl gr
Ob
Cl
Fag
Cor (F)
Tbe (B)
Timp
Solo
Ossia
Viol
Vle
Vel
Cb
Vcl e Cb
arco
div
in B
passionato
36
38
colla parte
a tempo
p sub
poco
pizz

39
Fl. gr.
Ob.
Cl.
Fag.
Cor. (F)
Solo
Viol.
Vle.
Vcl.
Cb.
I.
I. II.
p saltando
segue
div.
arco
pizz.
I. arco
I. arco
II. pizz.
41
cresc.
animato
40
II. pizz.
p espress.
unis. arco
p saltando
42

43
rallent.
Fl gr.
Ob.
Cl.
Fag.
Cor. (F)
Solo
Viol.
Vle.
Vcl.
Cb.
a 2
arco
div.
45
animando
rallent.
sempre sul G
a tempo
sul D
44
Tranquillo
I solo
sul G
dolce
unis.
dolcissimo
sul A
sul E
46
II. III.
poco
cresc. poco
cresc.
dolciss.
sul D

riten. poco a tempo
47
Fl. gr.
Ob.
Cl.
Fag.
Cor. (F)
Tbe. (B)
(in B)
Timp.
Solo
Viol.
pizz.
arco
Vle.
Vcl.
Cb.
(arco)
49
Solo
ten.
dim.
pizz.
Più sostenuto
arco
48
cadenza
in A
a piacere
Vcl. e Cb.
50
animato
I. II.
III.
cresc.
cresc. poco
Solo
(coperti)
(bouchés)

51
in A
Cl.
Fag.
Solo
Vcl. e Cb.
Tbe. (A)
Timp
Allegro ♩.=♩.=84 (ma poco sostenuto e pesante)
Cor. (F)
52
a 2.
a tempo
Viol.
Vle.
pizz.
53
Fl. p.
Fl. gr.
Ob.
Trgl.
Arpa
Vcl.
54

55
Fl.p.
Fl.gr.
Ob.
Cl.
Fag.
Cor. (F)
Tbe. (A)
Tbni.
Timp.
Trgl.
Arpa
Solo
Viol.
Vle.
Vcl.
Cb.
arco
div.
56
unis.
I.
57
I.
grazioso
pizz.
colla parte
a tempo
a piacere
cresc.
cresc. poco
dolce
Vcl. arco
Bassi pizz.
58
quasi Allegretto
Solo I.
espress.
Fl.gr.

59
animato poco
61
Fl.gr.
Ob.
Cl.
Fag.
Cor. (F)
Trgl.
Arpa
Solo
Viol.
Vle.
Vcl.
Cb.
Timp.
div.
pizz.
unis.
arco
60
62
Tbe. (A)
Tbni.

63
Fl.gr.
Ob.
Cl.
Fag.
Cor. (F)
Tbe. (A)
I.
Tbni.
Solo
Viol.
unis.
Vle.
Vcl.
Cb.
pizz.
65
Fl.gr.
Cl.
I.
III. IV.
Cor. (F)
Trgl.
Arpa
Solo
unis.
Viol.
pizz.
Vle.
Fl.gr.
Ob.
Cl.
Cor. (F)
Trgl.
Arpa
Solo
arco
Viol.
arco
Vle.
64
Fl.gr.
Ob.
Cl.
Fag.
I. II.
Cor. (F)
Arpa
Solo
pizz.
div.
Viol.
pizz.
div.
Vcl.
Cb.
66
Fl.gr.
I.
cantabile
Ob.
Cl.
cantabile
Fag.
a 2.
Cor. (F)
Trgl.
pizz.
Viol.
pizz.
arco
Vle.
pizz.
arco
pizz.
Vcl. e Cb.

67
Fl. gr.
Ob.
Cl.
Fag.
Cor (F)
Camp
Trgl.
Arpa
Solo
Viol.
Vle.
Vcl.
Cb.
69
I solo
tremolo
div.
(pizz.) div.
68
solo
70
dolciss.
I. II.
arco
div.

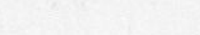

Fl.p. Fl.gr. Ob. Cl. Fag. Cor. (F) Tbe (A) Camp. Arpa Solo Viol. Vle Vcl.

cresc. f pp I. Sole sul G ff unis. pizz.

73

animando poco a poco

Fl.gr. Cl. Fag. Cor. (F) Solo Viol. Vle Vcl. Cb.

mf p dolce arco

72

Fl.p. Fl.gr. Ob. Cl. Fag. Cor. (F) Camp. Arpa Solo Viol. Vcl. e Cb.

II pp cresc. a 2 mf pizz.

74

Fl.gr. Ob. Cl. Fag. Arpa Solo Viol. Vle Vcl. Cb.

p mf div. pizz.

75
Fl.p.
Fl.gr.
Ob.
Cl.
Cor. (F)
Arpa
Solo
Vle
Vcl.
Cb.
77
più animato
Timp.
Viol.
pizz.
unis.
76
sempre animando
Fag.
78
cresc.
arco
div.

79
Fl. gr.
Ob.
Cl.
Fag.
Cor. (F)
Tbe. (A)
Timp.
Trgl.
Piat.
Solo
Viol.
Vle.
Vel.
Cb.
p sub.
ff
tr
80
Fl. p.
Fl. gr.
Ob.
Cl.
Fag.
Cor. (F)
Tbe. (A)
Camp.
Trgl.
Piat.
Arpa
Solo
pizz.
f (quasi guitarra)
Viol.
Vle.
Vcl. e Cb.
81
Fl. p.
Fl. gr.
Ob.
Cl.
Fag.
Cor. (F)
Tbe. (A)
Camp.
Arpa
Solo
pizz.
Viol.
Vle.
Vcl.
82
Fl. p.
Fl. gr.
Ob.
Cl.
Fag.
Cor. (F)
Camp.
Arpa
Solo
Viol.
Vle.
Vcl.

83
Cl.
Fag.
Tbni.
Solo
arco
sul G
f pesante
Viol.
Vle.
Vcl.
(sempre più animando)
Fl. gr.
Ob.
Cor. (F)
Trgl.
pizz.
solo
85
♩ = 160
Tbe. (A)
Arpa
div.
84
Viol. I
arco
I. solo
Viol. II.
86
Cb.
pizz. div.

87
88
89
90
Fl. gr.
Ob.
Cl.
Fag.
Cor. (F)
Tbe. (A)
Tbni.
Timp.
Trgl.
Arpa
Solo
Ossia
Viol.
Vle.
Vcl.
Cb.
Vcl. e Cb.
a 2
I.
cresc.
arco
pizz.
div.
unis.
unis. pizz.
sempre animando
poco

91
Fl. gr.
Cl.
Fag.
Cor. (F)
Timp.
Solo
Viol.
Vle.
Vcl. e Cb.
92
Fl. p.
Fl. gr.
Cl.
Fag.
Cor. (F)
Timp.
Trgl.
Solo
Viol.
Vle.
Vcl.
Cb.
dim.
pizz.
unis.
93
Fl. p.
Fl. gr.
Ob.
Cl.
Fag.
Trgl.
Solo
Viol.
Vle.
Vcl.
a 2
cresc. poco
div.
unis.
94
Fl. gr.
Cor. (F)
Solo
Viol.
Vle.
Vcl. e Cb.
Cl.
Fag.
Tbe. (A)
cresc.
poco
pizz.

95
Fl. gr.
Ob.
Cl.
Fag.
Cor. (F)
Tbe. (A)
Timp.
Trgl.
Arpa
Solo
Viol.
Vle.
Vcl. e Cb.
arco
pizz.
I. solo
I.
96
a 2
I. II.
Ossia
(arco)
97
Fl. p.
Tbni.
Camp.
Piat.
mf cresc.
p cresc.

ÉDOUARD LALO

SYMPHONIE ESPAGNOLE, Op. 21 *Score P. 165*

The composition of this work was begun by Édouard Lalo immediately after the successful première of his Concerto in F major for violin by Sarasate at the Concert National, Paris in 1874. Sarasate was also the soloist at the first performance of the *Symphonie Espagnole,* which took place at a concert of the Association Artistique under Édouard Colonne at the Châtelet in Paris on Feb. 7, 1875. On Nov. 30, 1878, Sarasate gave the English première of the work at the Crystal Palace, London.

The melodic beauty, vivacious rhythms and generally inspiring character of the concerto aroused the admiration not only of the musical public, but also of many of Lalo's confrères. Hans von Bülow gave it preference over Bruch's second violin concerto, and Tschaikowsky wrote as follows about it to his friend, Mme. von Meck: "Do you know the *Symphonie Espagnole* by the French composer, Lalo? This piece has recently been brought out by the very modern violinist, Sarasate. . . . The work has given me the greatest pleasure; it is so delightfully fresh and light, with piquant rhythms and beautifully harmonized melodies. Like Delibes and Bizet, Lalo shuns carefully all that is *routinier,* seeks new forms without wishing to be profound, and cares more for musical beauty than for the old traditions."

Symphonie Espagnole

Édouard Lalo

1

3

2

4

5
A
Fl.picc.
Fl.
Ob.
Cl.
Fag.
Cor.
Tb.
Trbi.
Tp.
Vl.
Vla.
Vc.
Cb.
7
B
Solo
Vl.pr.
Vc. e Cb.
6
8
largamente
pizz.

9
Ob.
Cl.
Fag.
Cor. (D)
Tp.
Vl.pr.
f espress.
pizz.
Vl.
Vla.
Vc. e Cb.
cresc.
arco
mf espress.
11
Fl.
Tb. (D)
ff ben sost.
Cb.
10
pesante
12
Cor.
(B)
Trbi.
pesante ben sost.

C
Fl.picc.
Fl.
Ob.
Cl.
Fag.
Cor.
Tb.
Trbi.
Vl.pr.
Vl.
Vla.
Vc.
Cb.
a II
III
pesante
dolce espress.
div.
pizz.
Vc. e Cb.
D
Tp.
Solo
unis.
arco
cresc.
dolce
dim.

17
Fl.
Ob.
Cl.
Fag.
a II
Vl. pr.
cresc.
Vla.
Vc.
pizz.
E
a II
I
Cor. (B)
Tp.
Vl.
div. pizz.
unis.
arco
pizz.
18
Ob.
Fag.
I
Vl. pr.
Vl.
Vla.
Vc. e Cb.
Cl.
(D)
Cor.
(B)
III
Cb.
19
I Solo
Solo
cresc.
20
Fl. picc.
Fl.
Cor. (D)
Tb. (D)
arco

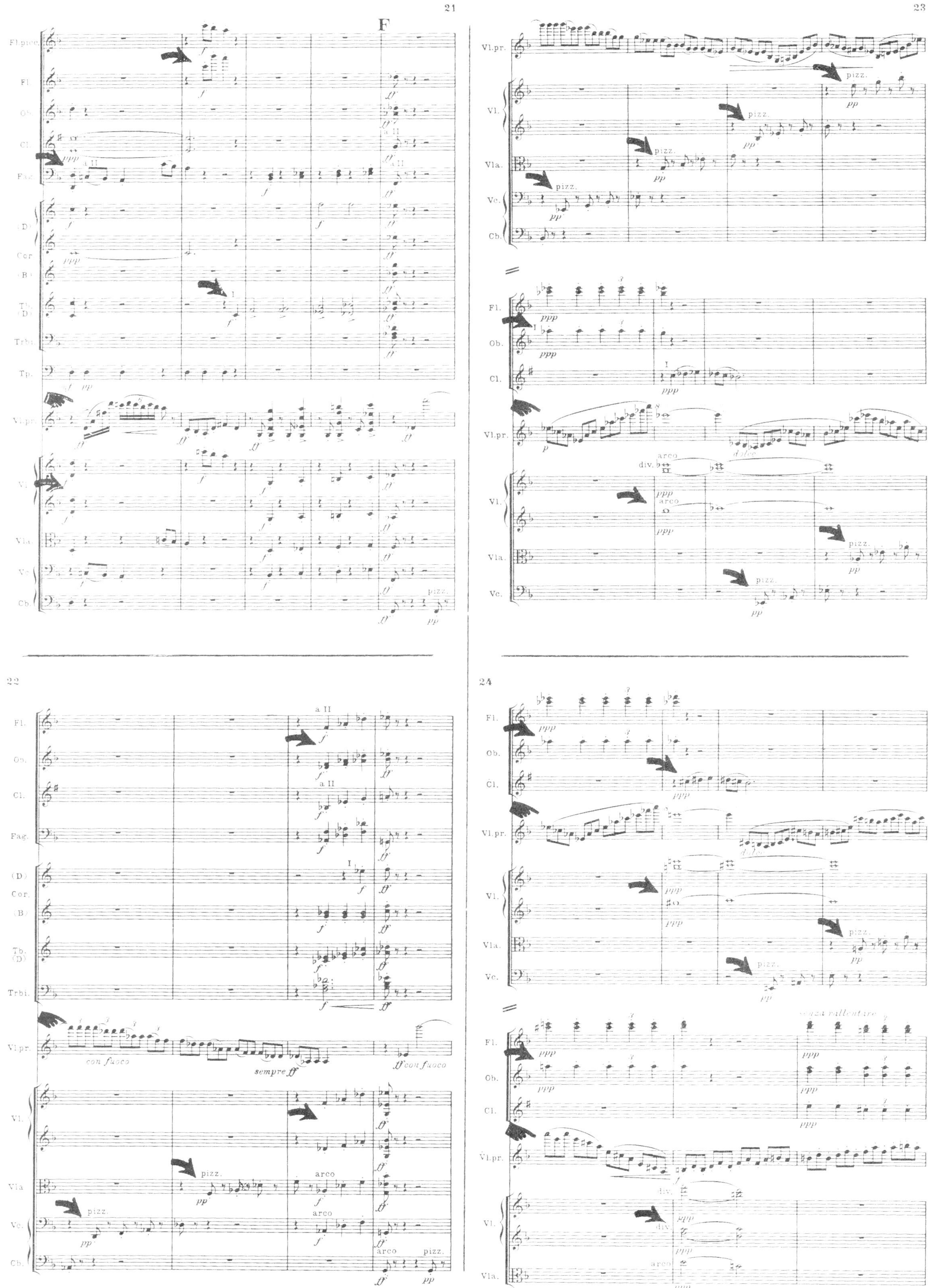

21
F
Fl. picc.
Fl.
Ob.
Cl.
Fag.
Cor.
Tb.
Trbi.
Tp.
Vl. pr.
Vl.
Vla.
Vc.
Cb.
a II
pizz.
22
con fuoco
sempre ff
ff con fuoco
arco
23
div.
dolce
24
senza rallentare

25
26
27
28
G
Fl.picc.
Fl.
Ob.
Cl.
Fag.
(D)
Cor.
(B)
Tb.
(D)
Trbi.
Tp.
Vl.pr.
Vl.
Vla.
Vc.
Cb.
Vc.
e Cb.
a II
I
unis.
arco
pizz.
cresc.
ff
f
p
ppp
pp

29
Fl.
Ob.
Cl.
Fag.
Cor. (D)
Tp.
Vl.pr.
f espress.
pizz.
Vl.
Vla.
Vc.
Cb.
30
mf espress.
arco
cresc.
31
32
H
pesante
arco
Vc. e Cb.
Tb. (D)
Cor. (B)

33
35
34
36
Cl.
Fag.
Cor. (D)
Vl. pr.
Vla.
Vc. e Cb.
Tp.
Vl.
Fl.
Ob.
Trbi.
Vl. I.
Tb. (D)
Vc.
Cb.
dolce espress.
cresc.
p dim.
div.
pizz.
arco
unis.
sempre ppp
dolce
a II
ben sost.
sempre cresc.

37
Fl.picc.
Fl.
Ob.
Cl.
Fag.
(D) Cor. (B)
Tb. (D)
Trbi.
Tp.
Vl.
Vla.
Vc.
Cb.
cresc.
38
Fl.
Cl.
Fag.
Tp.
Vl.pr.
ff ben marcato
tempo stretto
Vc. e Cb.
Cor (D)
f ben sost.
pizz.
39
arco
div.
pizz.div.
40
a II
unis.
unis. arco

II
Scherzando
Allegro molto (♪=200)
41
43
42
44
2 Flauti
2 Oboi
2 Clarinetti in B
2 Fagotti
I. II in G
4 Corni
III. IV in E
2 Trombe in D
3 Tromboni
Timpani in D-G
Triangolo
Arpa
Violino princ.
Violino I
Violino II
Viola
Violoncello
Contrabasso
A
Solo
mf espress.
pizz.
arco
div.
unis.
sec.
a II
ten.

45
47
46
48
B
Fl.
Ob.
Cl.
Fag.
Tp.
Trgl.
Arpa
Vl. pr.
Vl.
Vla.
Vc.
Cb.
a II
sec.
div.
unis.
ten.

49
51
50
52
C
Fl.
Ob.
Cl.
Fag.
Cor.
Tb.
Trbi.
Tp.
Trgl.
Arpa
Vl. pr.
Vl.
Vla.
Vc.
Cb.
sec.
a II
a III
ten.
dolce
f espress.
arco
pizz.

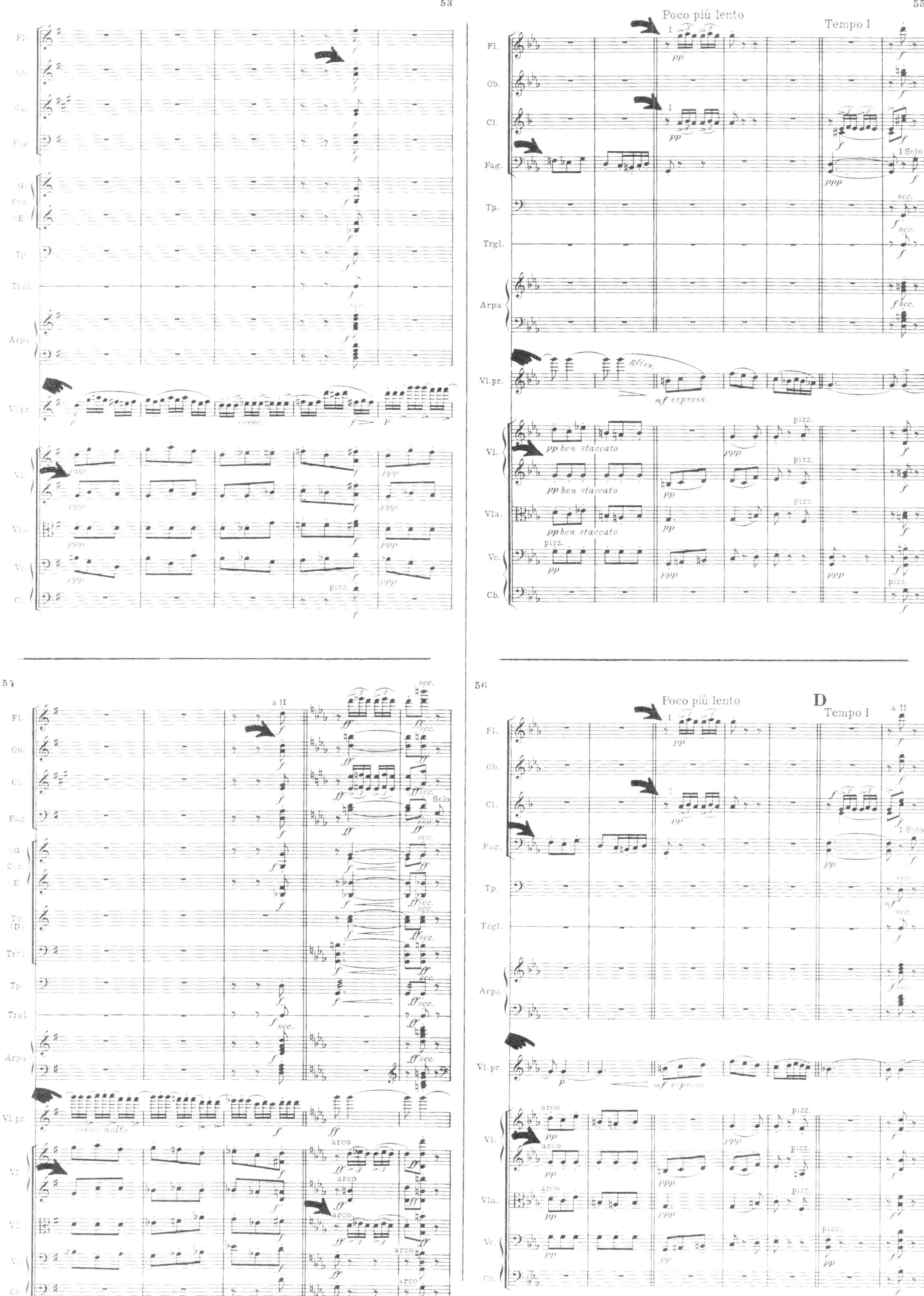

53
55
Poco più lento
Tempo I
54
56
D
Fl.
Ob.
Cl.
Fag.
Cor. (E)
Tp.
Trgl.
Arpa
Vl.pr.
Vl.
Vla.
Vc.
Cb.
Tr. (D)
Trbi.
pp ben staccato
mf espress.
gliss.
cresc. molto
I Solo
pizz.
arco
sec.
a II

57
Poco più lento
Tempo I
a II
I ten.
ten.
ten.
I.Solo
sec.
Fl.
Ob.
Cl.
Fag.
Tp.
Trgl.
Arpa
Vl. pr.
dolce
arco
pizz.
Vl.
Vla.
Vc.
Cb.
59
Poco più lento
mf espress.
Tempo I
58
Poco più lento
Tempo I
Solo
mf espress.
60
Poco più lento
Tempo I
I Solo
Poco più lento
Tempo I
f Solo

E Poco più lento
61
rit.
Fl.
Ob.
Fag.
Tp.
Vl. pr.
Vc.
cresc.
rall.
dim.
Vl.
Vla.
arco
a tempo mosso
pizz.
Vl. I
63
F
a II
Cl.
Cor.
Trgl.
Arpa
sec.
espress.
ten.
Cb.
62
Tempo I
Tb. (D)
Trbi.
64
div.
unis.
mf espress.

65
66
67
68
G
Fl.
Ob.
Cl.
Fag.
Tp.
Trgl.
Arpa
Vl. pr.
Vl.
Vla.
Vc.
Cb.
a II
I
div.
unis.
sec.
rit.
cresc.
f espress.
ten.
arco
div. pizz.
pizz.

69
Tempo I
Cl.
Fag.
Tp.
Trgl.
Arpa
Vl.pr.
dolce
pp dolciss.
unis. ten.
arco
pizz.
Vl.
Vla.
unis.
Vc.
Cb.

III
Intermezzo
Allegretto non troppo (♩= 66)
71
Flauto picc.
2 Flauti
2 Oboi
2 Clarinetti in B
2 Fagotti
I. II in A
4 Corni
III. IV in E
2 Trombe in D
3 Tromboni
Timpani in E-A
Violino princ.
Violino I
Violino II
Viola
Violoncello
Contrabasso
a II
sec.

70
Vl.pr.
espress.
Vl.
Vla.
Vc.
Fl.
Ob.
Fag.
I. Solo
Cor. (G)
Tp.
Trgl.
Vl. pr.
pizz.
Cb.

72
Fl.
Ob.
Fag.
Cor. (A)
Tp.
Vl.
Vla.
Vc. e Cb.

73

Fl. picc.
Fl.
Ob.
Fag.
Cor. (A)
Tb. (D)
Tp.
Vl.
Vla.
Vc. e Cb.

74

Fl. picc.
Fl.
Ob.
Cl.
Fag.
(A) Cor. (E)
Tb. (D)
Trbi.
Tp.
Vl.
Vla.
Vc. e Cb.
a II

75

A
Fl. picc.
Fl.
Ob.
Cl.
Fag.
(A) Cor. (E)
Tb. (D)
Trbi.
Tp.
Vl. pr.
Solo espress.
ben sost.
Vl.
Vla.
Vc. e Cb.
a II
sec.
pizz.

76

Tp.
Vl. pr.
Vl.
Vla.
Vc.
Cb.
pizz.
Fl.
Fag.
p dolce
div.

Fl.
Fag.
Tp.
Vl.pr.
Vl.
Vla.
Vc.
Cb.
Cl.
Cor. (E)

B
Fl.
Ob.
Cl.
Fag.
Tp.
Vl.pr.
Vl.
Vla.
Vc.
Cb.

78

Fl.
Ob.
Cl.
Fag.
Cor. (E)
Tp.
Vl.pr.
Vl.
Vla.
Vc.
Cb.

80

Fl.
Ob.
Cl.
Fag.
Cor. (A)
Tp.
Vl.pr.
Vl.
Vla.
Vc.
Cb.

81
83
82
84
Fl. picc.
Fl.
Ob.
Cl.
Fag.
Cor. (A)
Cor. (E)
Tb. (D)
Trbi.
Tp.
Vl. pr.
Vl.
Vla.
Vc.
Cb.
Vc. e Cb.
C
Un poco più lento
appassionato
sempre
ben sost.
pizz.
arco
sec.
a II
III IV
III

85
87
D
rall.
Fl.
Ob.
Cl.
Fag.
Vl. pr.
Vl.
Vla.
Vc.
Cb.
a tempo
cresc.
pizz.
Fl. picc.
Cor.
(A)
(E)
Tb.
(D)
Trbi.
Tp.
a II
a III
sec.
e Cb.
86
88
arco
Vc. arco

Fl.picc.
Fl.
Ob.
Cl.
Fag.
(A) Cor. (E)
Tb. (D)
Trbi.
Tp.
Vl. pr.
Vl.
Vla.
Vc. e Cb.
Vc.
Cb.
sec.
a II
arco
pizz.
pp
ppp
ff
cresc.
rall.
a tempo
pesante
dolce
90
92
*) In der Viol.-Solostimme:

93
Fl.
Fag.
Tp.
Vl. pr.
Vl.
Vla.
Vc.
Cb.
E
Cl.
Cor. (E)
dolce
div.
unis.
arco

95
Fl.
Ob.
Cl.
Fag.
Cor. (E)
Tp.
Vl. pr.
Vl.
Vla.
Vc.
Cb.
sempre cresc.
accelerando
cresc.

94
Fl.
Ob.
Cl.
Fag.
Cor. (E)
Tp.
Vl. pr.
Vl.
Vla.
Vc.
Cb.
dolce
cresc.
arco

96
F
Cl.
Vl. pr.
Vl.
Vla.
Vc.
Cb.
espress.
appassionato
rit.
Tempo I un poco più lento poco rit.
Fl.
Ob.
dim.
dolce
div.
arco

97
Tempo I
Fl.picc.
Fl.
Ob.
Cl.
Fag.
(A) Cor. (E)
Tb. (D)
Trbi.
Tp.
Vl. pr.
Vl.
Vla.
Vc.
Cb.
a II
pizz.
arco
99
A
ten.
ben sostenuto espress.
unis.
98
IV
Andante (♩= 60)
2 Flauti
2 Oboi
2 Clarinetti in B
2 Fagotti
I. II
4 Corni in F
III. IV
2 Trombe in D
3 Trombomi
Timpani D-A
Violino princ.
Violino I
Violino II
Viola
Violoncello
Contrabasso
ben sostenuto
div.
(Quattro da segno C con sordini)
100
Cor. (F)
Solo espress.
ben sost.
cresc.

101
B
rall.
a tempo
Fl.
Ob.
Cl.
Fag.
Cor. (F)
Tb. (D)
Trbi.
Tp.
Vl. pr.
Vl.
Vla.
Vc.
Cb.
Solo
espress.
cresc.
dim.
arco
pizz.
102
C
ten.
con sordino
Vl. II.
appass.
103
a tempo
slargando
dolce
uniz.
pizz
104
D
espress.
tranquillo

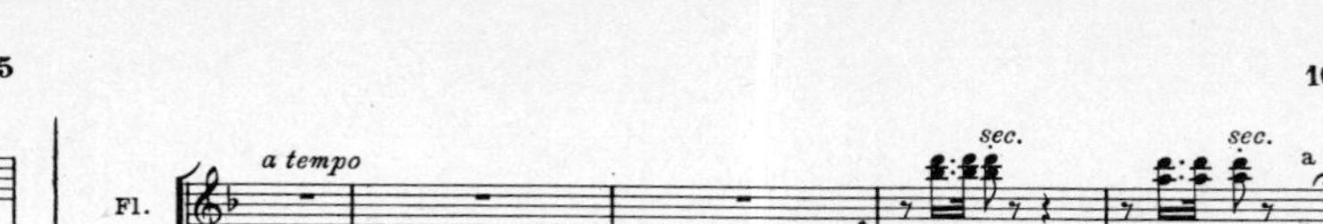

105

Fl. Ob. Cl. Fag. Cor. (F) Tb. (D) Trbi. Tp. Vl. pr. Vl. Vla. Vc. Cb.

a II — p cresc. — rit. — cresc. — f — arco — p cresc. — pp

107

a tempo — sec. — ff — a II — ben sostenuto — f — lib. — a tempo lib. — pp

Fl. Ob. Cl. Fag. Cor. (F) Tb. (D) Trbi. Tp. Vl. pr. Vl. Vla. Vc. e Cb.

106

Fl. Ob. Cl. Fag. Cor. (F) Tb. (D) Trbi. Tp. Vl. pr. Vl. Vla. Vc. e Cb.

f — tr — senza sordino — senza sordino — senza sordino — senza sordino.

108

E

I — ppp — cresc. — a tempo — f — pp — pizz.

Cl. Tp. Vl. pr. Vl. Vla. Vc. Cb.

cresc. — cresc. — appassionato

109
110
111
112
V
Rondo
Allegro
Flauto picc.
2 Flauti
2 Oboi
2 Clarinetti in A
2 Fagotti
I.II in D
4 Corni
III.IV in F
2 Trombe in D
3 Tromboni
Timpani D-A
Tamburo
Triangolo
Arpa
Violino princ.
Violino I
Violino II
Viola
Violoncello
Contrabasso
con sordino
a tempo
lib.
rall.
dolce
cresc.
dim.
sec.
pizz.
arco

113
Fl.picc.
Fl.
Ob.
Cl.
Fag.
(D) Cor. (F)
Tb. (D)
Tp.
Tamb.
Trgl.
Ap.
Vl.
Vla.
Vc.
Cb.
cresc.
arco
115
p dim.
ppp
III.IV
Cor. (F)
Vl.pr.
giojoso
Solo
pizz.
114
Trbi.
dim.
116
A
Vl.II
Vc. e Cb.

117
119
118
120
B
rit.
a tempo
Fl.
Ob.
Cl.
Fag.
Cor. (F)
Tp.
Tamb.
Trgl.
Vl.pr.
Vl.
Vla.
Vc. e Cb.
Tb. (D)
Cb.
III. IV
pizz.

121
Fl.
Ob.
Cl.
Fag.
(D) Cor. (F)
a II
Tb. (D)
Trbi.
Tp.
Vl.pr.
Vl.
Vla.
Vc.
arco
Cb.
pizz.
122
C
123
Vl. I.
Vc. e Cb.
Tamb.
124
poco rit.
D
a tempo
cresc.
III.IV
sempre ppp
sempre ff
p cresc.
III
Trgl.

125
Cl.
Fag.
Tamb.
Trgl.
Vl.pr.
Vl. I.
Vla.
Vc. e Cb.
arco
Fl.
Ob.
Cl.
Vl.pr.
Vl. I.
Vla.
Vc.
Cb.
pizz.
126
Fl.
Ob.
Cl.
a II
Vl.pr.
Vl.
Vc.
arco
Fl.
Vl.pr.
Vl.
Vc.
pizz.
127
Fl.picc.
Fl.
Ob.
Cl.
a II
Fag.
Vl.pr.
Vc. e Cb.
pizz.
Cl.
Fag.
Tamb.
sempre
Vl.pr.
pizz.
Vl.
Vla.
Vc. e Cb.
cresc.
128
E
poco rit.
a tempo
Ob.
Cl.
Fag.
cresc.
Tamb.
Vl.pr.
arco
Vl.
Vla.
Vc.
Cb.
Cl.
Fag.
Tp.
Tamb.
Trgl.
Vl.pr.
Vl.
Vla.
Vc.
Cb.

Fl.
Cl.
Fag.
Vl. pr.
Vl.
Vc.
Cb.
ppp
senza rallentare
Fl. picc.
Ob.
Arpa
cresc.
pizz.
130
F
Cl.
a II
ff
(D)
Cor.
(F)
Tb.
(D)
Trbi.
Tp.
Tamb.
Trgl.
arco
Vla.
mf
p
132
III.IV
pp
Vc.
e Cb.

133
Fl.
Ob.
Cl.
Vl. pr.
Vl.
Vla.
Vc. e Cb.
Fag.
Vc.
135
Fl. picc.
Fl.
Ob.
Cl.
Fag.
(D) Cor. (F)
Tb. (D)
Trbi.
Tp.
Tamb.
Trgl.
Arpa
Vl. pr.
Vl.
Vla.
Vc.
Cb.
a II
134
G
Poco più lento (♩. = 96)
a II
a III
136
pizz.
arco

rit. **H** rall. Poco più lento (♩. = 78)

Fl. Ob. Cl. Fag. Vl. pr. Vl. Vla. Vc. Cb.

pp pizz. arco appassionato mf ppp

Vl. pr. Vl. Vla. Vc. Cb.

cresc. f dolce ppp

138

Cor. (F) Vl. pr. Vl. Vla. Vc. Cb.

III mf pp p ppp poco cresc. cresc.

poco rit. a tempo espress. dolce

cresc. f p pp mf dim. arco ppp

Fl. Ob. Cl. Trgl. Vl. pr. Vl. Vla. Vc. Cb.

ppp dolcissimo cresc. pizz.

a II cresc. ppp dolcissimo

140

poco rit.

Fl. Ob. Cl. Cor. (F) Trgl. Vl. pr. Vl. Vla. Vc. Cb.

ppp III mf pp a II cresc. pp

I a tempo

Fl. Vl. pr. Vl. Vla. Vc. Cb.

mf ppp cresc. f espress. dolce pp arco

141
poco a poco acceler.
sempre dolce
accelerando
143
poco rit.
J
a tempo
142
Tempo I (Allegro)
144

Fl.
Ob.
Cl.
a II
Vl. pr.
Vl.
Vc.
arco
ppp
K
a tempo
Tamb.
Trgl.
Tp.
Fag.
Vla.
Cb.
Fl. picc.
pizz.
pp
146
cresc.
Vc. e Cb.
poco rit.
sempre
148
senza rallentare
Arpa
arco
ff

L
149
Fl. picc.
Fl.
Ob.
Cl.
a II
Fag.
Cor.
Tb.
Trbi.
Tp.
Tamb.
Trgl.
Arpa
Vl. pr.
Vl.
Vla.
Vc.
Cb.
151
Fl.
Ob.
Cl.
Fag.
III. IV
Cor. (F)
Vl. pr.
Vl.
Vla.
Vc. e Cb.
I
pizz.
arco
150
152
M
sec.
a II

153

Fl. Tamb. Vl.pr. Vl. Vla. Vc. Cb.

ppp pp p pizz. ppp pizz. ppp ppp

Fl. Ob. Tamb. Vl.pr. Vl. Vla.

I ppp ppp

155

Fl. Ob. Tamb. Vl.pr. Vl. Vla.

I ppp cresc. f pizz. ppp sempre pizz. ppp

Fag. Vl.pr. Vl.I Vla. Vc. Cb.

a II pp pizz. arco pizz. arco pp ppp arco ppp

154

Fl. picc. Fl. Ob. Cl. Fag. (D) Cor. (F) Tb. (D) Trbi. Tamb. Vl. pr. Vl. Vla. Vc. Cb.

sec. a II f ppp pp p arco pizz. ppp

156

Fag. Vl.pr. Vl. Vla. Vc. Cb.

pp pizz. ppp cresc. f pizz.

N

Fag. (D) Cor. (F) Tb. (D) Trbi. Tp. Tamb. Vl.pr. Vl. Vla. Vc. e Cb.

sec. f p pp ff arco p arco

157
Fag.
(D) Cor. (F)
Tb. (D)
Trbi.
Tp.
Tamb.
Vl. pr.
Vl.
Vla.
Vc. e Cb.
a II sec.
sec.
159
O
dolce
Vl. pr.
Vl.
Vla.
Vc.
Fl. picc.
Fl.
Trgl.
Arpa
pizz.
158
Fag.
(D) Cor. (F)
Tb. (D)
Trbi.
Tp.
Tamb.
Vl. pr.
Vl.
Vla.
Vc.
pizz.
dim.
160
Fl. picc.
Fl.
Ob.
Cl.
Fag.
(D) Cor. (F)
Tb. (D)
Trbi.
Tp.
Tamb.
Trgl.
Arpa
Vl. pr.
Vl.
Vla.
Vc.
Cb.
pizz.
arco
a II

CAMILLE SAINT-SAËNS

CONCERTO in B minor, Op. 61

Score P. 206

Camille Saint-Saëns has left an imposing array of works for violin and orchestra; they comprise the Concertos, Op. 20, Op. 58 and Op. 61 (the latter presented here) ; also the *Introduction and Rondo Capriccioso,* Op. 28, the *Romance,* Op. 48, the *Morceau de Concert,* Op. 62 and the *Caprice Andalou,* Op. 122. Little is heard, at least in the United States over the air or in concert, of any of these works except the Concerto Op. 61 and the *Introduction and Rondo Capriccioso,* Op. 28.

The Concerto Op. 61, written in 1880 and dedicated to Sarasate, who gave the work its first public performance, was published in 1881; it gained immediate favor with the musical public, and is frequently heard in concert and broadcast. While lacking in depth when compared with some of the concertos in this volume, its wealth of melody, inherent "aliveness" (as Watson Lyle, one of Saint-Saëns' biographers, puts it) and innumerable opportunities for virtuosic display combine to make it an alluring work for violinists.

Concerto in B minor, Op. 61

Camille Saint-Saëns

1

2

3

4

Fl.
Hb.
Cl.1er
Bons
Cors
Tromp.
Tromb.
Timb.
Viol.
Alt.
Vclles.
C. B.
arco

Fl.
Hb.
Cl.
Bons.
Cors
à 2
Tromp.
Tromb.
Timb.
Viol.
Alt.
pizz
p marcato
Vclles.
pizz.
arco
C. B.
pizz.

6

A
Fl.
Hb.
Cl.
Bons
Cors
Tromp.
Tromb.
Timb.
Viol.
Div.
Unis.
Alt.
Vclles.
C. B.

8

Fl.
Hb.
Cl.
Bons.
Cors
Tromp.
Tromb.
Timb.
Viol.
dim.
Alt.
arco
Vclles.
C. B.
pizz.

9

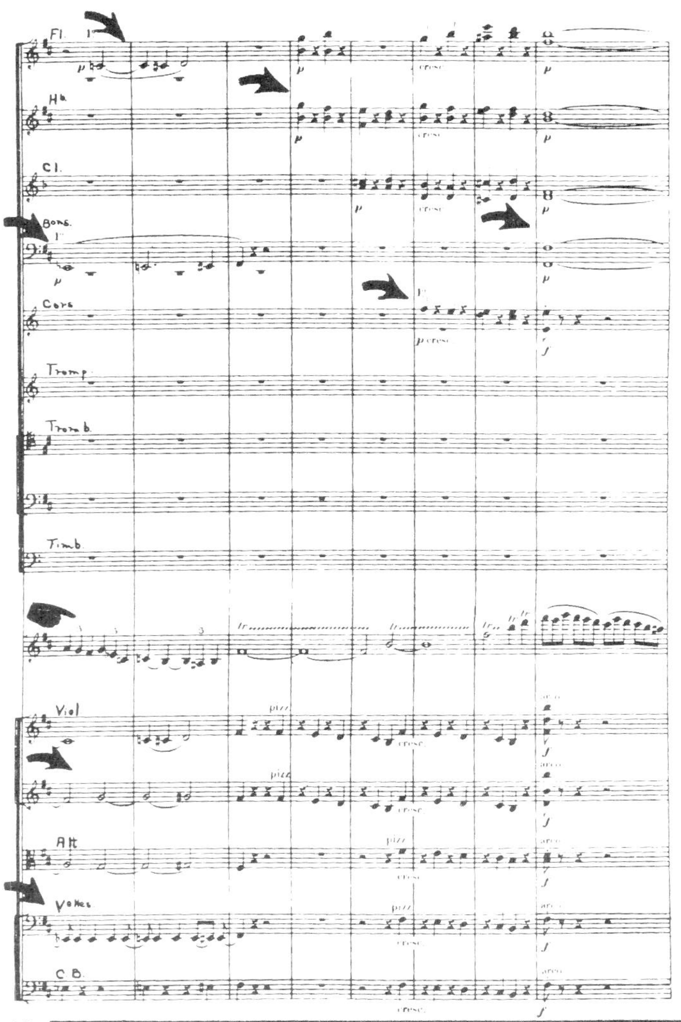

Fl. Hb. Cl. Bons. Cors Tromp. Tromb. Timb. Viol. Alt. Velles C.B.

pizz. arco cresc.

10

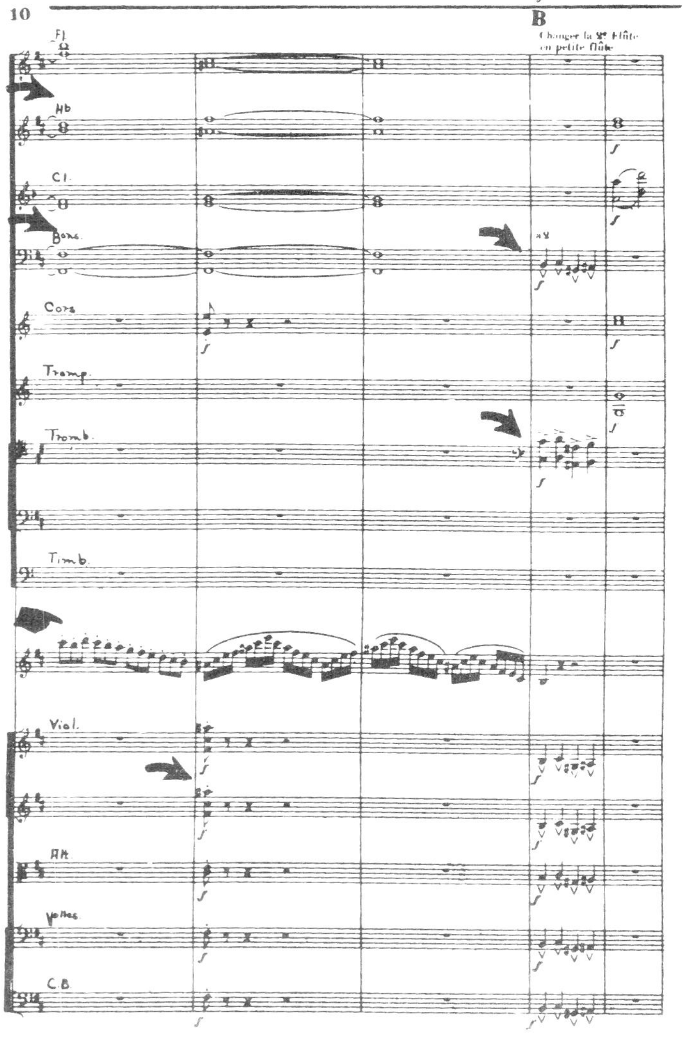

B

Changer la 2e Flûte en petite flûte

Fl. Hb. Cl. Bons. Cors Tromp. Tromb. Timb. Viol. Alt. Velles C.B.

11

12

Fl. Hb. à 2 Cl. Bons Cors à 2 Tromp. Tromb. à 2 Timb. Viol. Alt. Velles Col C.B. C.B.

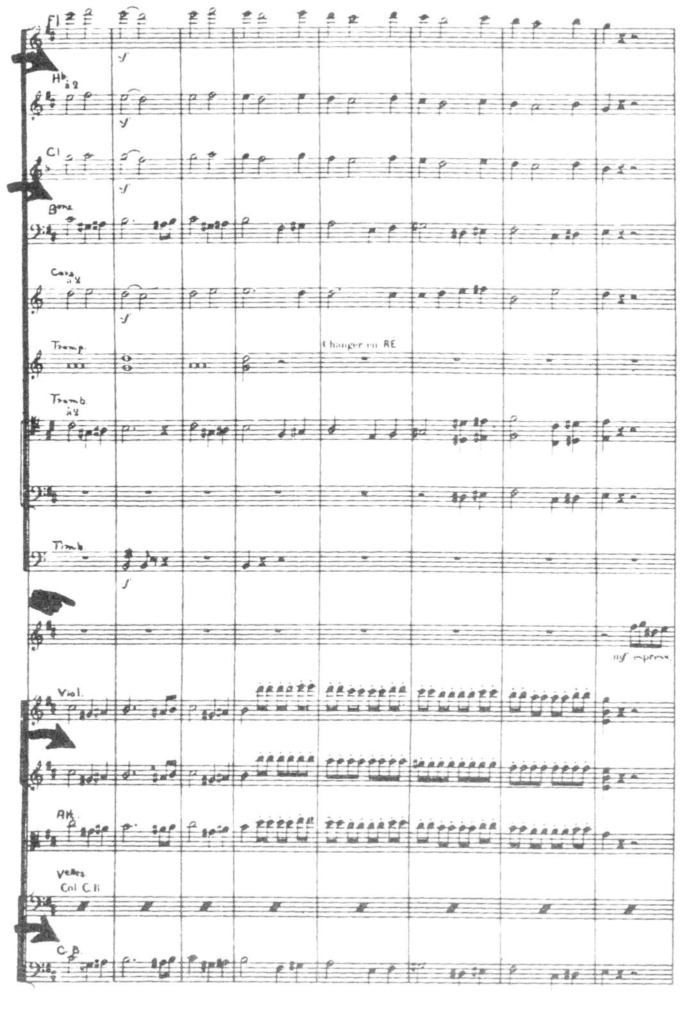

Changer en RÉ

mf impress.

Changer la petite flûte en grande flûte

2 Gdes flûtes

Hb.

Cl.

Bons.

Cors Changer en MI

Tromp.

Tromb.

Timb.

tranquillo assai

Viol.

Alt.

Vclles.

C. B.

14

Gdes Fl.

Hb.

Cl.

Bons.

Viol.

Alt.

Div.

Vclles.

C. B.

Fl.

Hb.

Cl.

Bons.

Cors en Mi.

dolce espressivo

Viol.

Div.

Alt.

Vclles et C.B.

pizz.

Cors en MI

dolcissimo

Viol.

Unis.

Alt.

Vclles.

arco

C. B.

Gdes Fl.

Cl.

Cors en MI

dim.

Viol.

Alt.

Vclles.

C. B.

arco

16

Fl.

Hb.

Cl.

Bons.

Cors

Tromp.

Tromb.

Timb.

calando

perdendosi

Viol.

pizz.

arco

Alt.

Div.

Vclles.

C. B.

17

C

Fl.
Hb
Cl.
Bons 1e
pp
Cors
Tromp.
Tromb.
Timb.
mf marcato
p
Viol.
Alt.
Unis.
Velles
arco
p
C.B.

18

Fl.
p
Hb
Cl.
Bons
Cors
1e
p
Tromp.
Tromb.
Timb.
Viol.
pizz.
arco
Alt.
pizz.
arco
Velles.
C.B.
pizz.
p

19

Hb.
1e
Cl.
Bons
1e
Cors
p
Viol.
pizz.
pizz.
Alt.
pizz.
Velles
Col C.B.
C.B.
pizz.

Fl.
Hb
Cl.
1e
Bons
Cors
Viol.
Alt.
Velles et C.B.

20

Fl.
Hb
Cl.
1e
pp
Bons
Cors
f
Viol.
pp
cresc.
pp
cresc.
Alt.
pp
cresc.
Velles et C.B.
cresc.

Fl.
Hb
1e
p
Cl.
p
Bons
1e
p
p
cresc.
Viol.
arco
mf
f
arco
mf
Alt. f
arco
mf
Velles et C.B.
f
arco
mf

Fl.
Hb.
Cl.
Bons.
Cors
Tromp. en RÉ
Tromb.
Timb.
Viol.
Alt.
Velles
Col C.B.
C.B.
p cresc.
cresc.
22
D
Cantabile
Changer en MI
tranquillo assai
dim.
Div.
Unis
Velles et C.B.
24
pizz.
dol.

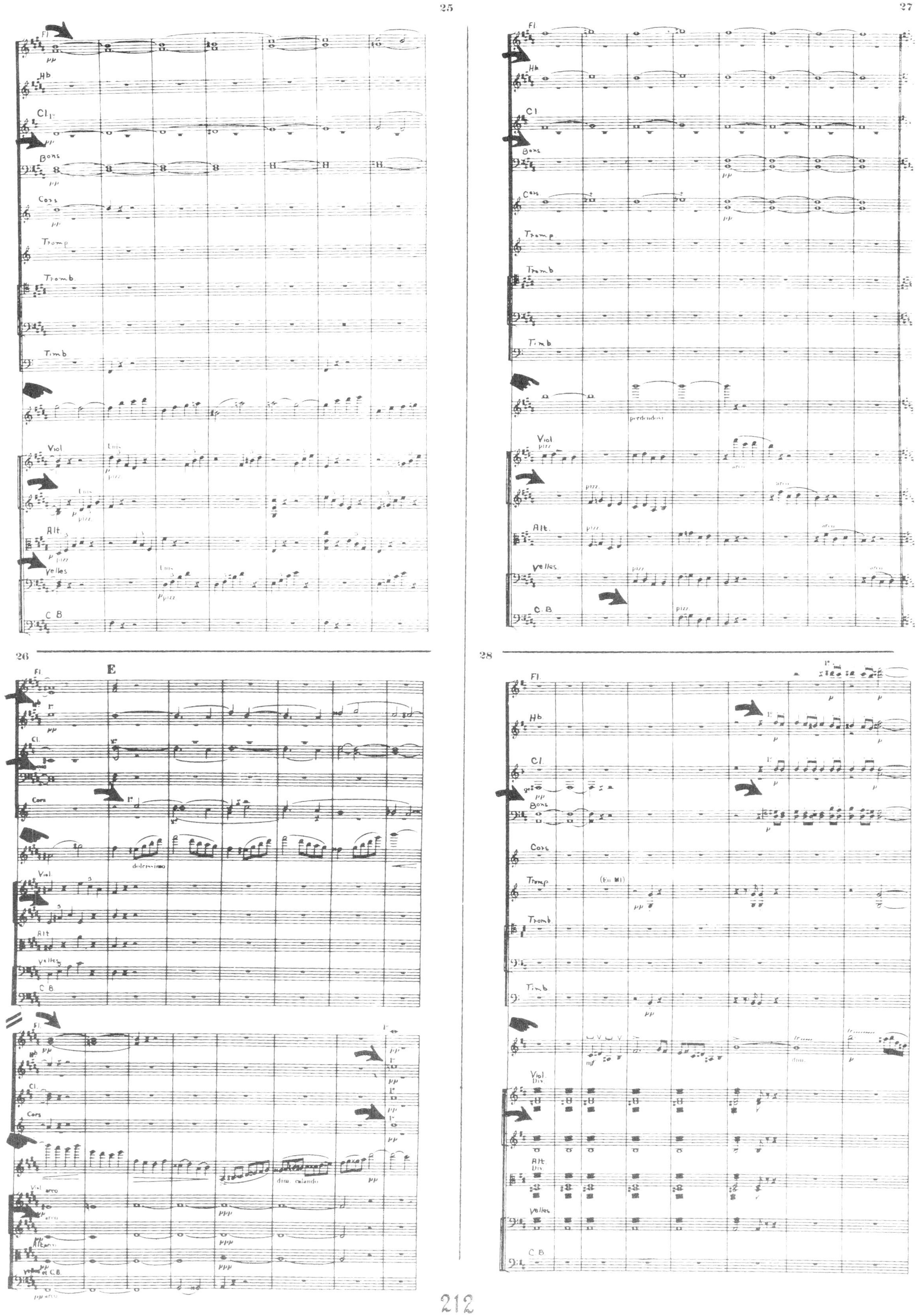

Fl.
Hb
Cl 1o
Bons
Cors
Tromp
Tromb
Timb
Viol
Unis
pizz.
Alt.
Velles
C. B

27

26

E

Fl.
Cl.
Cors
dolcissimo
Viol
Alt
Velles
C. B

Fl.
Hb
Cl.
Cors
dim. calando
Viol arco
Alt arco
Velles et C. B

28

29

F
Fl.
Hb.
Cl.
Bons.
Cors
Tromp.
Tromb.
Timb.
cresc.
Viol.
pizz.
arco
Alt.
Vlles pizz.
arco
C.B.
pizz.
arco

30

Fl.
Hb.
Cl.
Bons.
Cors
Tromp.
Tromb.
Timb.
Viol.
Div.
Div.
Alt.
Vlles.
C.B.
pizz.

31

Fl.
Hb.
Cl.
Bons.
Cors
Tromp.
Tromb.
Timb.
Viol.
Alt.
Vlles.
C.B.

32

Fl.
Hb.
Cl.
Bons.
Cors
Tromp.
Tromb.
Timb.
Viol.
Alt.
Vlles.
C. B.
arco

33

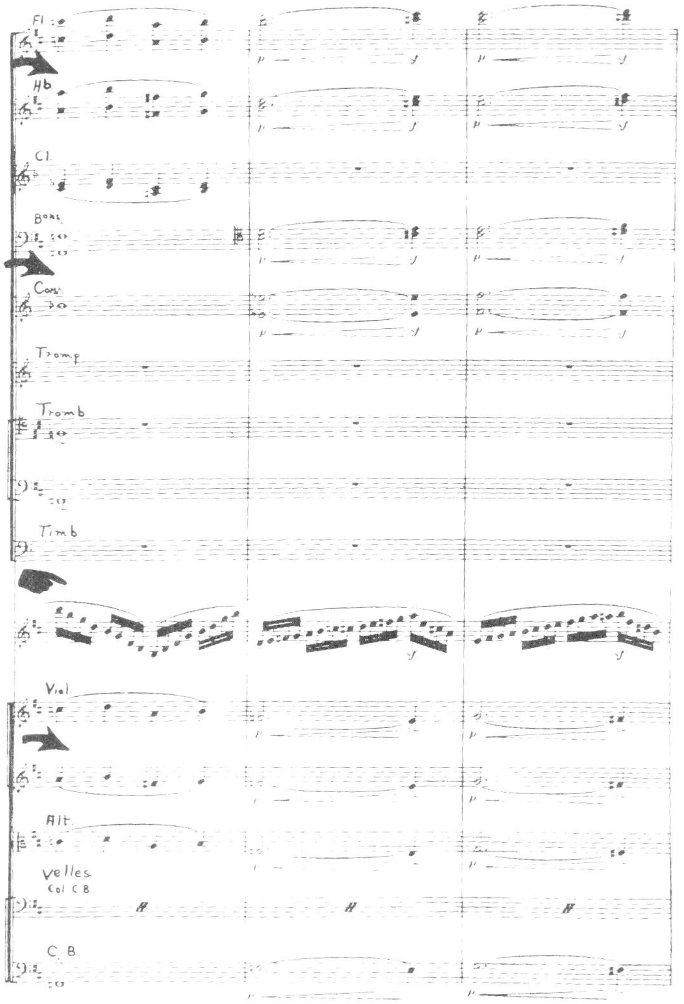
Fl.
Hb.
Cl.
Bons.
Cors
Tromp
Tromb
Timb
Viol.
Alt.
Velles
Col C B
C.B.

35

G
Fl.
Hb.
Cl.
Bons.
Cors
Tromp
Tromb.
Timb.
Viol.
Alt.
Velles
C.B.
dim.

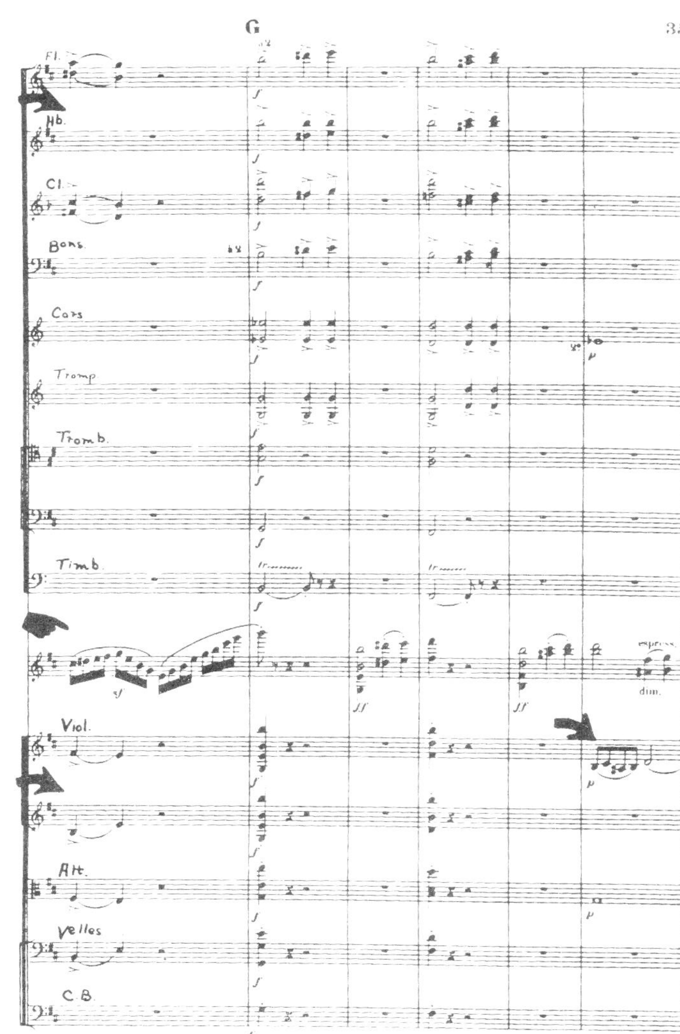

34

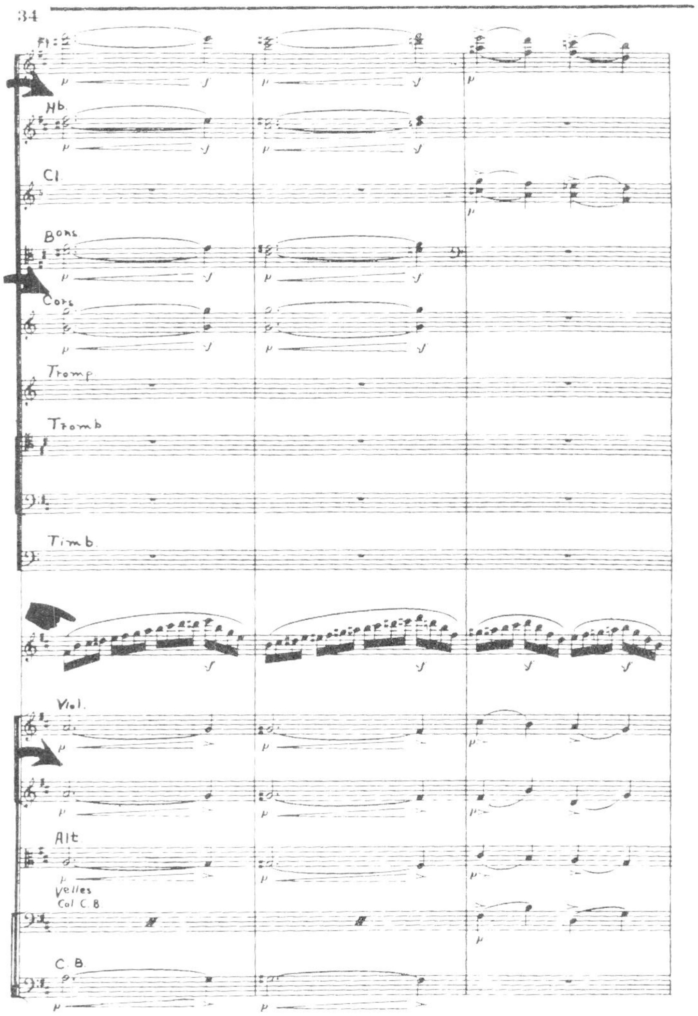
Fl.
Hb.
Cl.
Bons.
Cors
Tromp
Tromb
Timb
Viol.
Alt
Velles
Col C B
C B

36

Fl.
Hb
Cl.
Bons
Cors
Viol.
Alt.
Velles
C.B.
pizz.

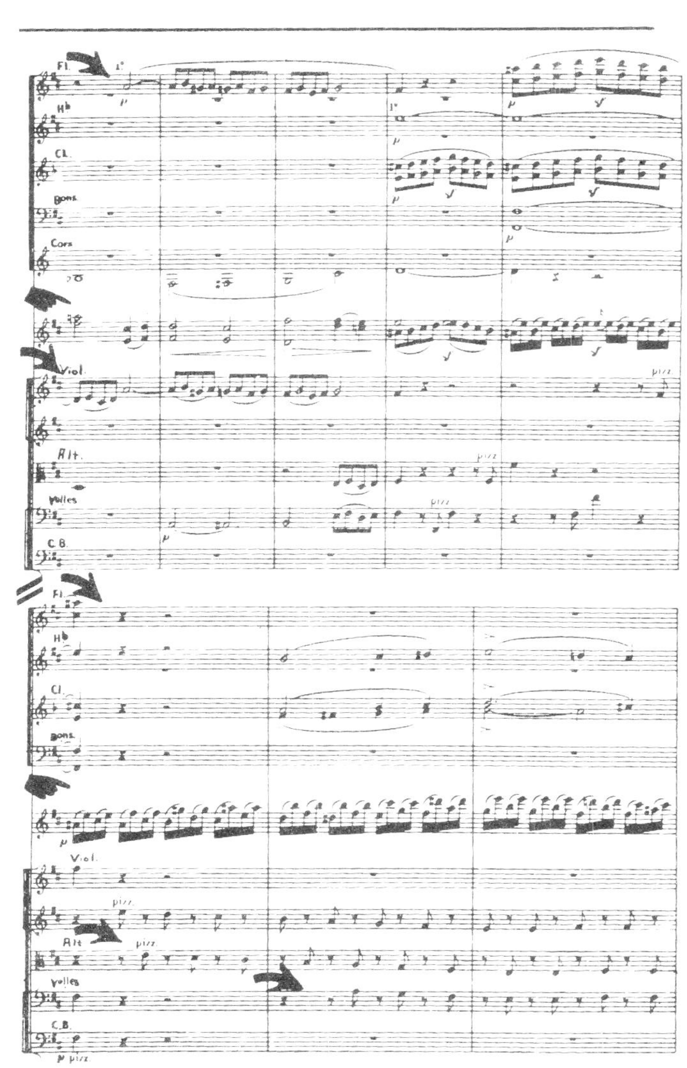

37

Fl.
cresc.
Hb.
Cl.
Bons.
Cors.
p
Tromp.
Tromb.
Timb.
Viol.
Alt
Velles.
Col C.B.
C.B.
(pizz)

38

Fl.
sp
Hb.
Cl.
Bons.
Cors.
Tromp.
Tromb.
Timb.
Viol.
arco
Alt.
Velles.
Col C.B.
C.B.
arco

39

Fl.
sp
Hb.
Cl.
Bons.
Cors.
Tromp.
Tromb.
Timb.
Viol.
Alt.
Velles.
Col C.B.
C.B.

40

Fl.
Hb.
Cl.
Bons.
Cors.
Tromp.
Tromb.
Timb.
Viol.
Alt.
Velles.
Col C.B.
C.B.

41
II

Andantino quasi all^tto (56 = ♩.)
2 FLÛTES
2 HAUTBOIS
2 CLARINETTES en SI♭
2 BASSONS
2 CORS en FA
(chromatiques)
Andantino quasi all^tto
semplice
VIOLON SOLO
VIOLONS
Div.
Unis.
ALTOS
VIOLONCELLES
pizz.
CONTREBASSES

42
Fl
1r
dol.
Hb
Cl
Bons
Cors
Viol
Alt
Velles.
C.B

43
Fl
Hb
Cl
dol
Bons
Cors
Viol.
Alt
Velles.
C.B.

44
Fl. 1r
Hb
Cl.
Bons
Cors
Viol.
Alt
Velles
C.B.
arco
Hb
Cl.
Cors
dim.
Viol
Alt
Velles et C.B.

A

45

Fl. 1r p
Hb.
Cl. 1r p
Cors pp
Viol. pp
Alt. pp
Velles.
C.B. pizz.

Hb. 1r pp
Bons pp
Cors pp
poco cresc.
Viol.
Alt.
Velles.
C.B.

46

Fl. pp
Hb. 1r p pp fp
Cl. 1r p fp
Bons. pp fp
Cors pp p fp
p pp
Viol. p
Alt.
Velles.
C.B.

49

B Fl. Hb. Cl. Bons. Cors Viol. Alt. Velles C.B.

50

Fl. Hb. Cl. Bons. Cors Viol. Alt. Velles C.B.

51

52

Fl.
Hb.
Cl.
Bons.
Cors
Viol.
Alt.
Velles.
C. B.

Fl.
Hb.
Cl.
Bons.
Cors
Viol.
Alt.
Velles.
C. B.

54

Fl.
Hb.
Cl.
Bons.
Cors
Viol.
Alt.
Velles.
C. B.

56

C
Fl.
Hb.
Cl.
Bons.
Cors
dim.
Viol.
dim.
Alt. pizz.
Velles.
C. B.

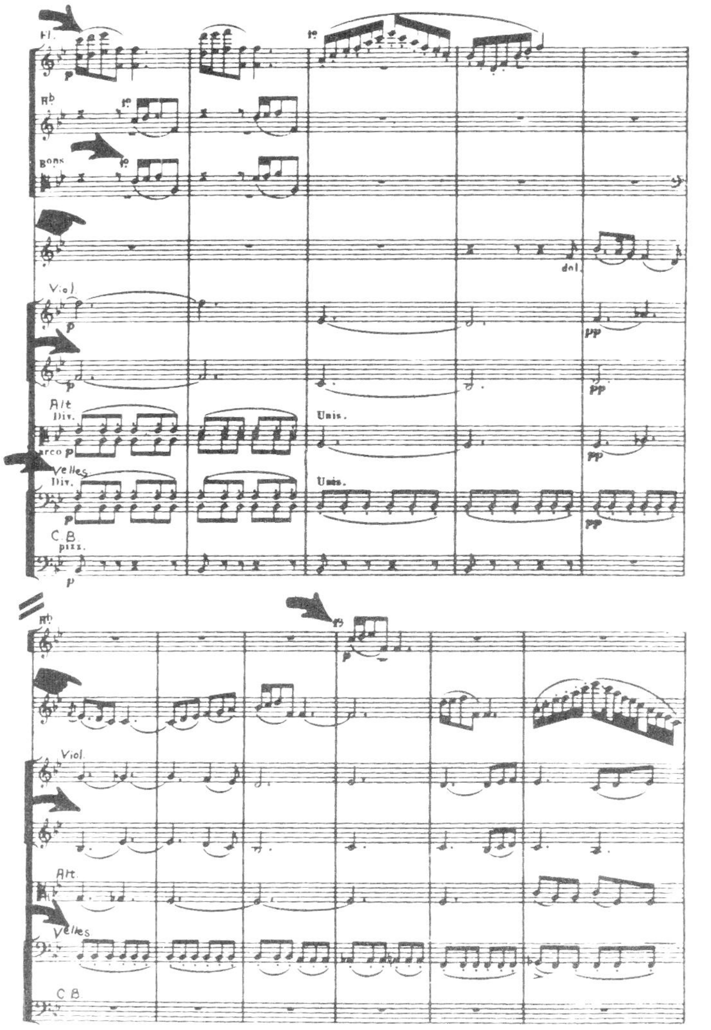

57

Fl.
Hb
Bons
Viol.
Alt
Div.
arco
Velles
Div.
Unis.
C.B.
pizz.
dol.
p
pp

Hb
Viol.
Alt.
Velles
C.B.

59

58

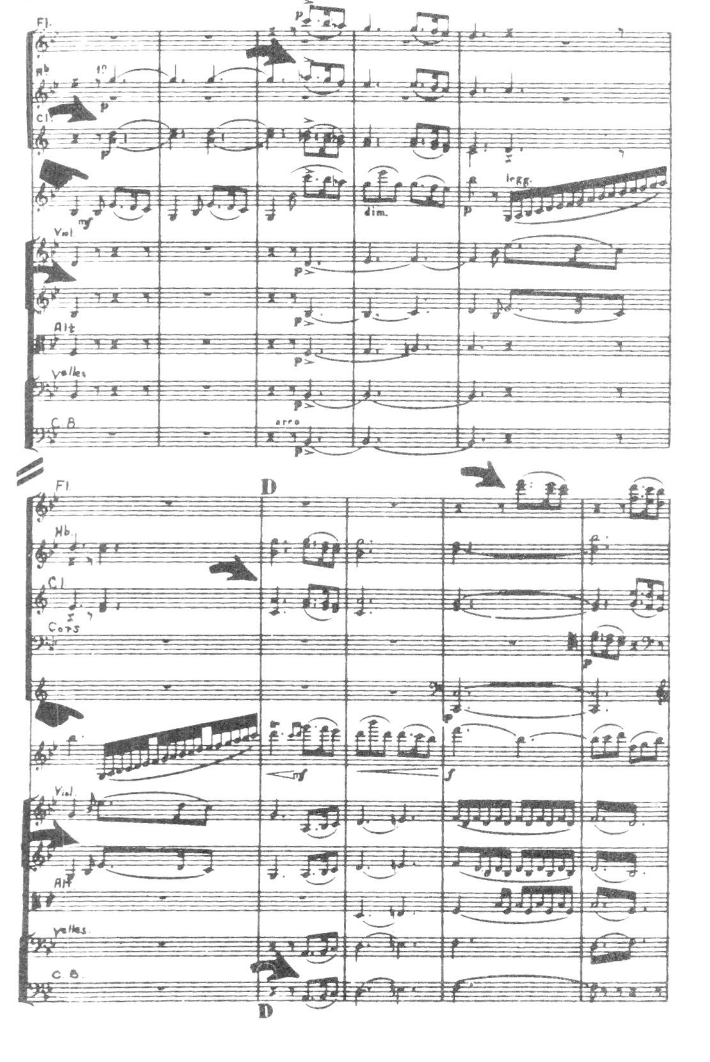

Fl.
Hb
Cl.
Viol
Alt
Velles
C.B.
arco
mf
dim.
legg.
p

Fl
D
Hb.
Cl
Cors
Viol.
Alt
Velles
C.B.
mf
f
D

60

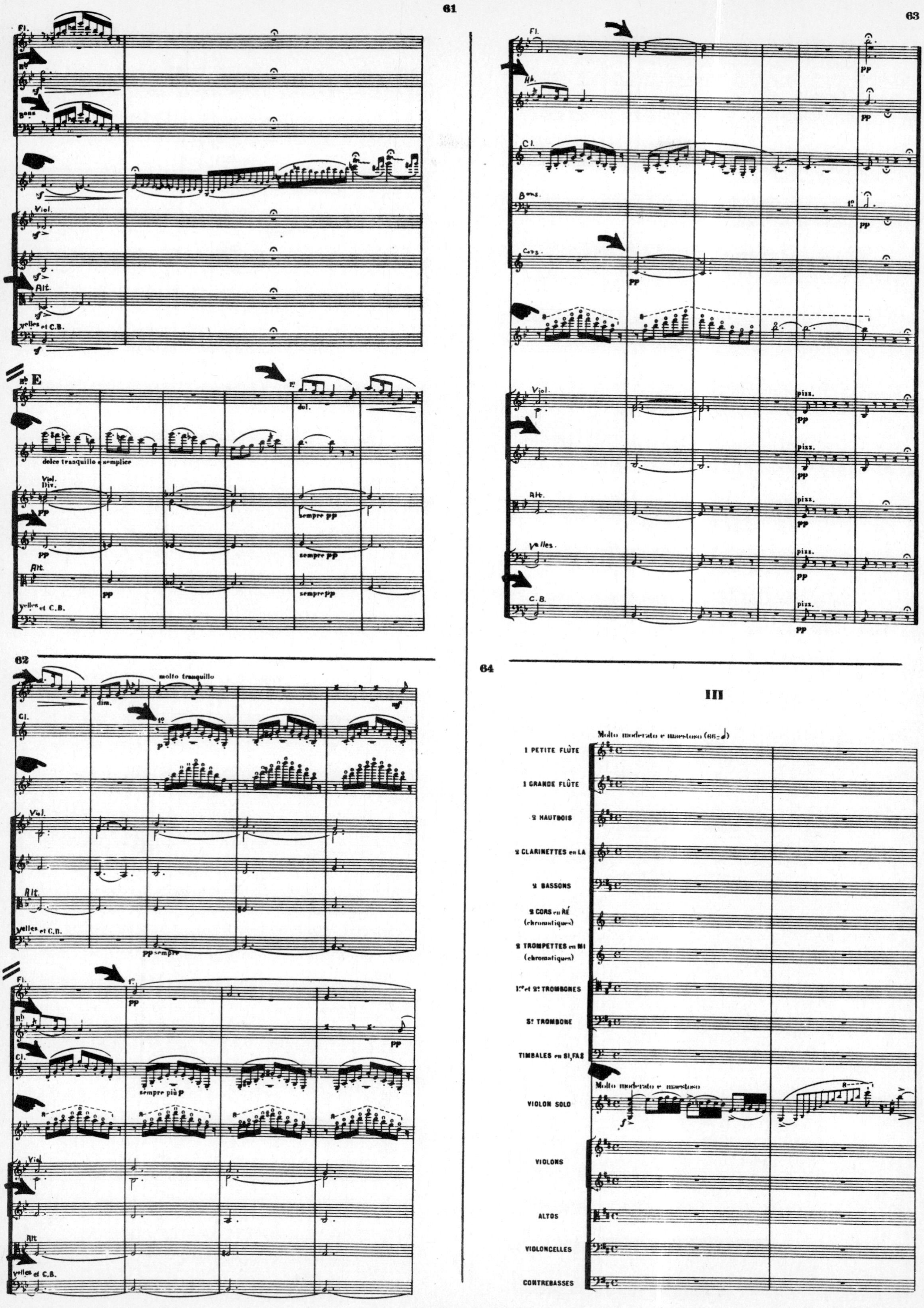

61

Fl.

Hb

Bons

Viol.

Alt.

Velles et C.B.

E

Fl.

dol.

dolce tranquillo e semplice

Viol. Div.

pp

sempre pp

Alt.

Velles et C.B.

62

molto tranquillo

dim.

Cl.

Viol.

Alt.

Velles et C.B.

pp sempre

Fl.

Hb

Cl.

sempre più p

Viol

Alt

Velles et C.B.

64

III

Pte. Fl.
Gde. Fl.
Hb.
Cl.
Bons.
Cors.
Tromp.
Tromb.
Timb.
Viol.
Alt.
Velles.
C.B.
Più mosso
ad lib.
dim.
pizz.
marcato
arco
All° non troppo
66
68

Pte. Fl.
Gde. Fl.
Hb.
Cl.
Bons.
Cors
Tromp.
Tromb.
Timb.
Viol.
Alt.
Velles.
C.B.
arco

70

72

73

Hb. Cl. Bons pp Viol. pp arco legg. pp Alt. Vcelles et C.B.

Hb. p Cl. p Cors p cresc. Viol. pizz. p Alt. Vcelles et C.B.

74

Gde Fl. p Hb. p Cl. Bons p Cors dim. p Viol. arco Alt. arco Vcelles et C.B.

Cl. Bons Cors p Viol. pp pp Alt. Vcelles C.B.

75

Cl. Bons Cors cresc. Viol. pizz. Alt. Vcelles et C.B.

B

Gde Fl. p Hb. p Cl. p Bons Cors f Viol. Alt. Vcelles et C.B.

76

Pte Fl. f Gde Fl. f Hb. f Cl. f Bons f p Cors f Tromp. Tromb. Timb. Ossia Viol. pizz. Div. arco p Div. arco p Alt. pizz. arco f Div. p Vcelles arco f Div. p C.B. arco f

77

79

Pte. Fl.
Gde. Fl.
Hb.
Cl.
Bons.
Cors
Tromp.
Tromb.
Timb.
Viol.
Alt.
Vcelles.
C.B.
f fp p

78

80

Pte. Fl.
Gde. Fl.
Hb.
Cl.
Bons
Cors
Tromp.
Tromb.
Timb.
Viol.
Alt.
Vcelles
C.B.
cresc.
p f

81

Pte Fl.
Gde Fl.
Hb
Cl.
Bons
Cors
Tromp.
Tromb
Timb
Viol
Div.
Alt
Velles
C. B.

83

C

Cl.
Bons
Cors
Viol
Alt
Velles et C. B.

Hb
Cl.
Bons
Cors
cresc.
Viol
Alt
Velles et C. B.

82

Pte Fl.
Gde Fl.
cresc.
Hb
Cl.
Bons
Cors
Tromp.
Tromb.
Timb
Viol
Unis.
Alt.
Velles
C. B.

84

Hb
Cl.
Bons
Cors
Viol
Alt
Div.
Velles
C. B.

Cl.
Bons
Tromp.
Tromb
cresc.
Viol
Alt.
Unis.
Velles et C. B.

85

Pte. Fl.
Gde. Fl.
Hb.
Cl.
Bons.
Cors
Tromp.
Tromb.
Timb.
Viol.
Alt.
Vcelles Col C.B.
C.B.

p f dim.

86

Gde. Fl. cresc. dim.
Hb. cresc. dim.
Cl. cresc. dim.
Bons. p cresc. dim.
Viol.
Alt.
Vcelles.
C.B.

Gde. Fl.
Hb.
Cl.
Bons.
Viol. dim.
Alt.
Vcelles. dim.
C.B.

87

Gde. Fl. pp
Hb. pp
Cl. pp
Bons. pp
Viol. con sordini cantabile pp
con sordini Div. pp
Alt. con sordini pp
Vcelles pp
C.B. pizz. pp

Viol.
Alt.
Vcelles et C.B. pizz. pp

88

Gde. Fl. pp
Hb. pp
Cl. pp
dolcissimo
Viol. sempre pianissimo
Alt.
Vcelles et C.B.

Gde. Fl.
Hb. pp
Cl.
D
Viol. poco cresc.
Div. poco cresc.
Alt. poco cresc.
Vcelles et C.B.

Viol.
pp
mf
dim.
pp
Alt.
Velles et C.B.

Gde Fl.
pp
p
Viol.
ppp
sempre pianissimo possibile
Alt.
Velles et C.B.

90

Gde Fl.
Hb.
Cl.
Bons
Riten.
a tempo
espressivo
dim.
Viol.
Alt.
Velles
C.B.
pizz.

Gde Fl.
Hb.
Cl.
Bons
Cors
legg.
Viol.
Alt.
Velles
C.B.
pp

Gde Fl.
Hb.
Cl.
Bons
Cors
senza sordini
Viol.
Alt.
Velles
C.B.
pp
pizz.

92

Hb.
Cl.
Bons
Cors
Viol.
Alt.
Velles et C.B.

Hb.
Cl.
Bons
Cors
poco a poco cresc.
Viol.
Alt.
Velles et C.B.

Pte. Fl.
Gde. Fl.
Hb.
Cl.
Bons.
Cors
Tromp.
Tromb.
Timb.
Viol.
Alt.
Velles.
Col C.B.
C.B.

p cresc. — cresc. — arco

Pte. Fl.
Gde. Fl.
Hb.
Cl.
Bons.
Cors
Tromp.
Tromb.
Timb.
Viol.
Alt.
Velles.
C.B.

p cresc. — à 2 — tr

94

E

Pte. Fl.
Gde. Fl.
Hb.
Cl.
Bons.
Cors
Tromp.
Tromb.
Timb.
Viol.
Alt.
Velles.
C.B.

f — ff — p

96

Pte. Fl.
Gde. Fl.
Hb.
Cl.
Bons.
Cors
Tromp.
Tromb.
Timb.
Viol.
Alt.
Velles.
C.B.

p cresc. — f — ff — tr

97
99
98
F
100
Pte Fl
Gde Fl
Hb.
Cl.
Bons
Cors
Tromp
Tromb.
Timb
Viol.
Alt.
Velles
C.B.
p cresc.
ff
sfp

Pte. Fl.
Gde. Fl.
Hb.
Cl.
Bons.
Cors
Tromp.
Tromb.
Timb.
dim.
Viol.
Alt.
Velles.
C. B.

Pte. Fl.
Gde. Fl.
Hb.
Cl.
Bons.
Cors
Tromp.
Tromb.
Timb.
legg.
cresc.
Viol.
Alt.
Velles.
pizz.
C. B.

Pte. Fl.
Gde. Fl.
Hb.
Cl.
Bons.
cresc.
Cors
Tromp.
Tromb.
Timb.
p cresc.
Viol.
Alt.
Velles.
arco
C. B.

G
Pte. Fl.
Gde. Fl.
Hb.
Cl.
Bons
Cors
Tromp.
Tromb.
Timb.
Viol.
pizz.
Alt.
Velles
Col C. B.
C. B.

105

107

Pte Fl.
Gde Fl.
Hb.
Cl.
Bons
Cors
Tromb.
Tromp.
Timb.
Viol.
Alt
Velles
Col C.B.
C.B.
pizz.
p cresc.
cresc.

106

108

Gde Fl.
Hb.
Cl.
Bons
Tromp.
Tromb.
Viol.
Alt.
Velles et C.B.

Gde Fl.
Cl.
Bons
Tromp.
Tromb.
dol.
Viol.
Alt.
Velles et C.B.

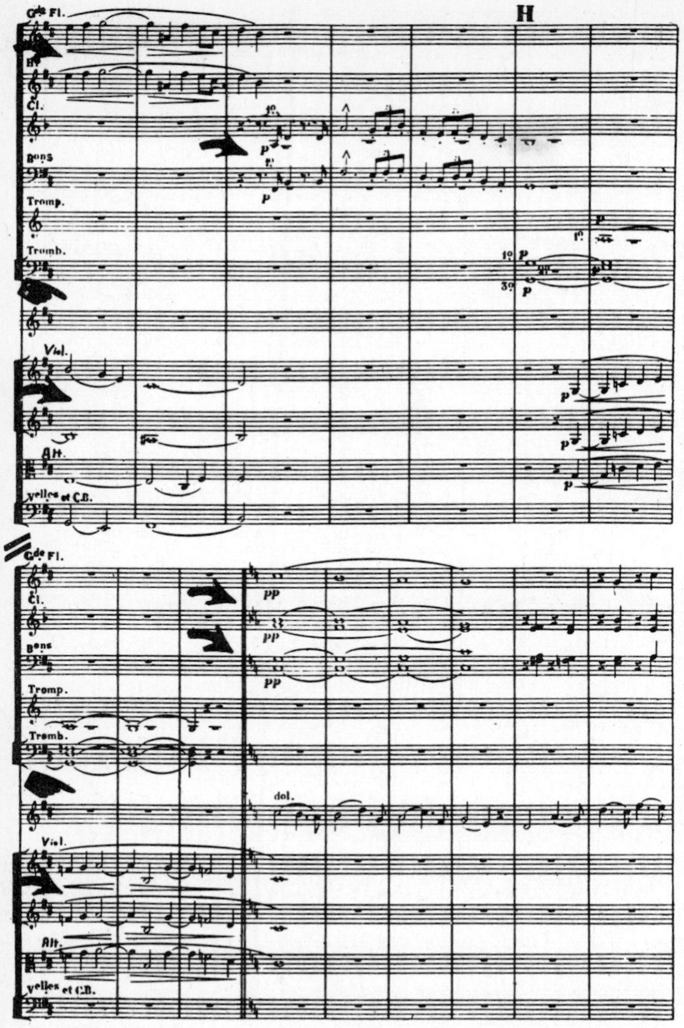

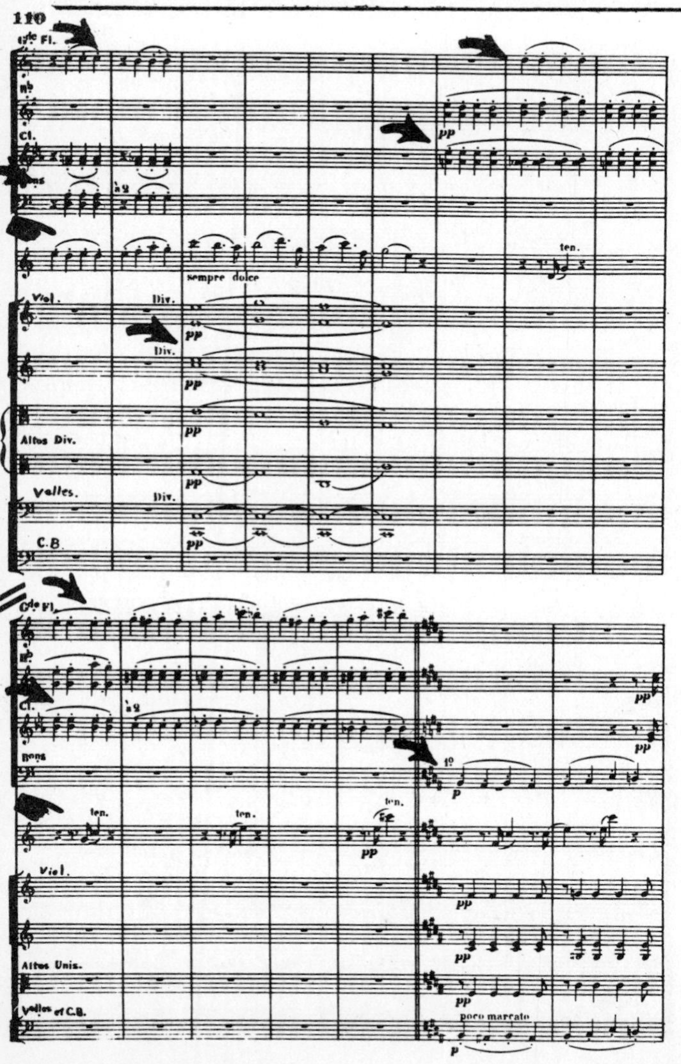

Gde Fl.
Hb.
Cl.
Bons
sempre dolce
ten.
Viol. Div.
Div.
Altos Div.
Velles. Div.
C.B.

Gde Fl.
Hb.
Cl.
Bons
ten.
Viol.
Altos Unis.
Velles et C.B.
poco marcato

113

Gde Fl.

Cl.

Bons

Cors

Tromp.

Viol.

Alt.

Velles et C.B.

Tromp.

Tromb.

Viol.

Alt.

Velles et C.B.

115

Gde Fl.

Hb.

Cl.

Bons

Cors

Tromp.

Tromb.

Timb.

I Viol. Div.

II Viol. Div.

Alt. Div.

Velles pizz.

C.B.

114

Tromp.

Tromb.

Viol.

Alt.

Velles et C.B.

Tromp.

Tromb.

Timb.

Viol.

Alt.

Velles et C.B.

116

Pte. Fl.

Gde Fl.

Hb.

Cl.

Bons

Cors

Tromp.

Tromb.

Timb.

I Viol.

II Viol.

Alt. Unis

Velles

C.B.

117

Hb. Cl. Cors Viol. Unis. pizz. Unis. pizz. Alt. pizz. Velles. C.B.

Gde Fl. Hb. Cl. Cors dim. poco a poco dim. Viol. Alt. Velles. C.B.

118

Gde Fl. Hb. Cl. Bons Cors Viol. Alt. Velles. C.B.

Gde Fl. Hb. Cl. Bons Cors Viol. Alt. Velles et C.B.

121

122

123

124

126

Pic. Fl.
Gde. Fl.
Hb.
Cl.
Bons.
Cors
Tromp.
Tromb.
Timp.
Viol.
Alt.
Vcelles.
C.B.
ff

PETER ILICH TSCHAIKOWSKY

CONCERTO in D major, Op. 35

Score P. 239

Tschaikowsky, while sojourning for the winter and spring of 1877 and 1878 in Italy and Switzerland, played a considerable amount of violin music with the Russian violinist, Joseph Kotek; it is more than probable that this inspired him to undertake the composition of a violin concerto, for he wrote to Mme. von Meck as follows about the first movement: "The plan of this movement sprang suddenly into my head, and quickly ran into its mould."

Several of the themes are Russian in character; he also commented on this to Mme. von Meck, saying that sometimes they were introduced intentionally and at other times spontaneously: "My melodies and harmonies of folk-song character come from the fact that I grew up in the country, and in my earliest childhood was impressed by the indescribable beauty of the characteristic features of Russian folk-music; also from this, that I love passionately the Russian character in all its expression; in short, I am a Russian in the fullest meaning of the word."

The concerto was first dedicated to Leopold Auer, at the time professor of violin at the St. Petersburg Conservatory, but Auer declined to play it on the ground that the technical difficulties were not only insurmountable, but that in many places the passage work was awkward and unviolinistic. The concerto therefore, although published, was neglected until another great virtuoso, Adolf Brodsky, a pupil of Hellmesberger, happened to see a copy of it, and after mastering its difficulties, played it at Vienna on Dec. 4, 1881, whereupon Tschaikowsky re-dedicated it to him. At a later period Auer changed his opinion, and virtuosos one by one gradually added the concerto to their repertories; at the present time it ranks in popularity with the Beethoven, Mendelssohn and Brahms concertos.

The work was received with bitter antagonism by critics and violinists alike; it is well worth while to quote in its entirety Eduard Hanslick's savage denunciation of it in his book entitled *The Beautiful in Music*: "The Russian composer, Tschaikowsky, certainly possesses no commonplace talent, but rather one which is forced, and which, labouring after genius, produces results which are tasteless and lacking in discrimination. Such examples as we have heard of his music (with the exception of the flowing and piquant Quartet in D) offer a curious combination of originality and crudeness, of happy ideas and wretched affectations. This is also the case as regards his latest long and pretentious Violin Concerto. For a time it proceeds in a regular fashion, it is musical and not without inspiration, then crudeness gains the upper hand and reigns to the end of the first movement. The violin is no longer played, but rent asunder, beaten black and blue. Whether it is actually possible to give clear effect to these hair-raising difficulties I do not know, but I am sure Herr Brodsky in trying to do so made us suffer martyrdom as well as himself. The Adagio, with its tender Slavonic sadness, calmed and charmed us once more, but it breaks off suddenly, only to be followed by a finale which plunges us into the brutal, deplorable merriment of a Russian holiday carousal. We see savages, vulgar faces, hear coarse oaths and smell fusel-oil. Friedrich Fischer, describing lascivious paintings, once said there were pictures 'one could see stink.' Tschaikowsky's Violin Concerto brings us face to face for the first time with the revolting idea: may there not also be musical compositions which we can hear stink?"

Concerto in D major, Op. 35
Peter Ilich Tschaikowsky
Allegro moderato. ♩ = 126.
Flauto I.
Flauto II.
2 Oboi.
2 Clarinetti in A.
2 Fagotti.
I. II.
4 Corni in F
III. IV.
2 Trombe in D.
Timpani in A-D.
Violino Solo.
Violino I.
Violino II.
Viola.
Violoncello.
Contrabasso.
poco a poco cresc.
pp cresc. poco a poco
marcato
piu f
cresc.
10
20

5
ritenuto
cresc.
f rit.
dim.
Moderato assai. ♩= 80
30
dolce
arco
pizz.
6
mf
cresc.
40
7
Ben sostenuto il tempo.
50
dim.
8
cresc.
V.S.
Vl.
Vla.
Vc.
Cb.

9
11
Fl.
Ob.
Cl. (A)
Fg.
Cor. (F)
Tbe. (D)
Timp.
V.S.
Vl.
Vla.
Vc.
Cb.
10
60
12
cresc.

13
15
14
16
70
80
90
V.S.
Vl.
Vla.
Vc.
Cb.
Cl. (A)
Cor. (F)
Ob.
Fg.
Fl.
dim.
con molto espr.
pizz.
arco
poco a poco cresc.
poco cresc.
I.II.
I. Solo
Bassi

17
19
18
20
100
I.
I.Solo
I.II.
Fl.
Cl. (A)
Ob.
Fg.
Cor. (F)
V.S.
Vl.
Vla.
Vc. Cb.
Cb.
poco cresc.
Più mosso.
Bassi

21
23
22
24
Ob.
Cl. (A)
Fg.
Cor. (F)
V. S.
Poco più lento.
Vl.
Vla.
Vc.
Cb.
cresc. poco a poco
pp poco a poco cresc.
Fl.
Tbe. (D)
Timp.
più mosso.

25
Fl.
Ob.
Cl. (A)
Fg.
Cor. (F)
Tbe. (D)
Timp.
V.S.
Vl.
Vla.
Vc.
Cb.
mf cresc.
cresc.
27
130
26
I. II.
Moderato assai.
ff
28

29
Fl.
Ob.
Cl. (A)
Fg.
Cor. (F)
Tbe. (D)
Timp.
V.S.
Vl.
Vla.
Vc.
Cb.
31
30
140
32

Fl.
Ob.
Cl. (A)
Fg.
Cor. (F)
Tbe. (D)
Timp.
V.S.
Vl.
Vla.
Vc.
Cb.
34
150
36
cresc.
mf
p
f

37
160
Fl.
Ob.
Cl. (A)
Fg.
Cor. (F)
Tbe. (D)
Timp.
V.S.
Vl.
Vla.
Vc.
Cb.
170
39
arco
pizz.
38
molto sostenuto il tempo, moderatissimo.
40
180

41
Ob.
Cl. (A)
Fg.
Cor. (F)
p cresc.
I. II.
V.S.
arco
Vl.
Vla.
Vc.
Cb.
Vc. Cb.
Bassi
43
190
Fl.
Tbe. (D)
Timp.
42
ff
44
f

45
47
46
48
200
Fl.
Ob.
Cl. (A)
Fg.
Cor. (F)
Tbe. (D)
Timp.
V.S.
Vl.
Vla.
Vc.
Cb.
cresc.

210
Fl.
Ob.
Cl. (A)
Fg.
Cor. (F)
Tbe. (D)
Timp.
V. S.
Cadenza
ff
Vl.
Vla.
Vc.
Cb.
a tempo
p
tr
dolce
pp
pizz.
arco
pp a tempo
cresc.
poco cresc.
50
ff legato
dim.
Quasi andante
cresc. e accelerando
meno mosso
52
220
15
mf

53
Cl. (A)
Fg.
V. S.
Vl.
Vla.
Vc.
Cb.
230
mf
f
dim. molto
f dim.
mf dim.
arco
55
240
Ob.
Cl. (A)
Fg.
Cor. (F)
I. II.
pizz.
cresc.
54
Ben sostenuto.
p grazioso
pp
cresc.
56
Fl.
Tbe. (D)
Timp.

57
59
Fl.
Ob.
Cl. (A)
Fg.
Cor. (F)
Tbe. (D)
Timp.
V.S.
Vl.
Vla.
Vc.
Cb.
arco
250
I. II.
con molto espress.
pizz.
58
60
Vc. Cb.
Bassi
260
cresc.
p cresc.

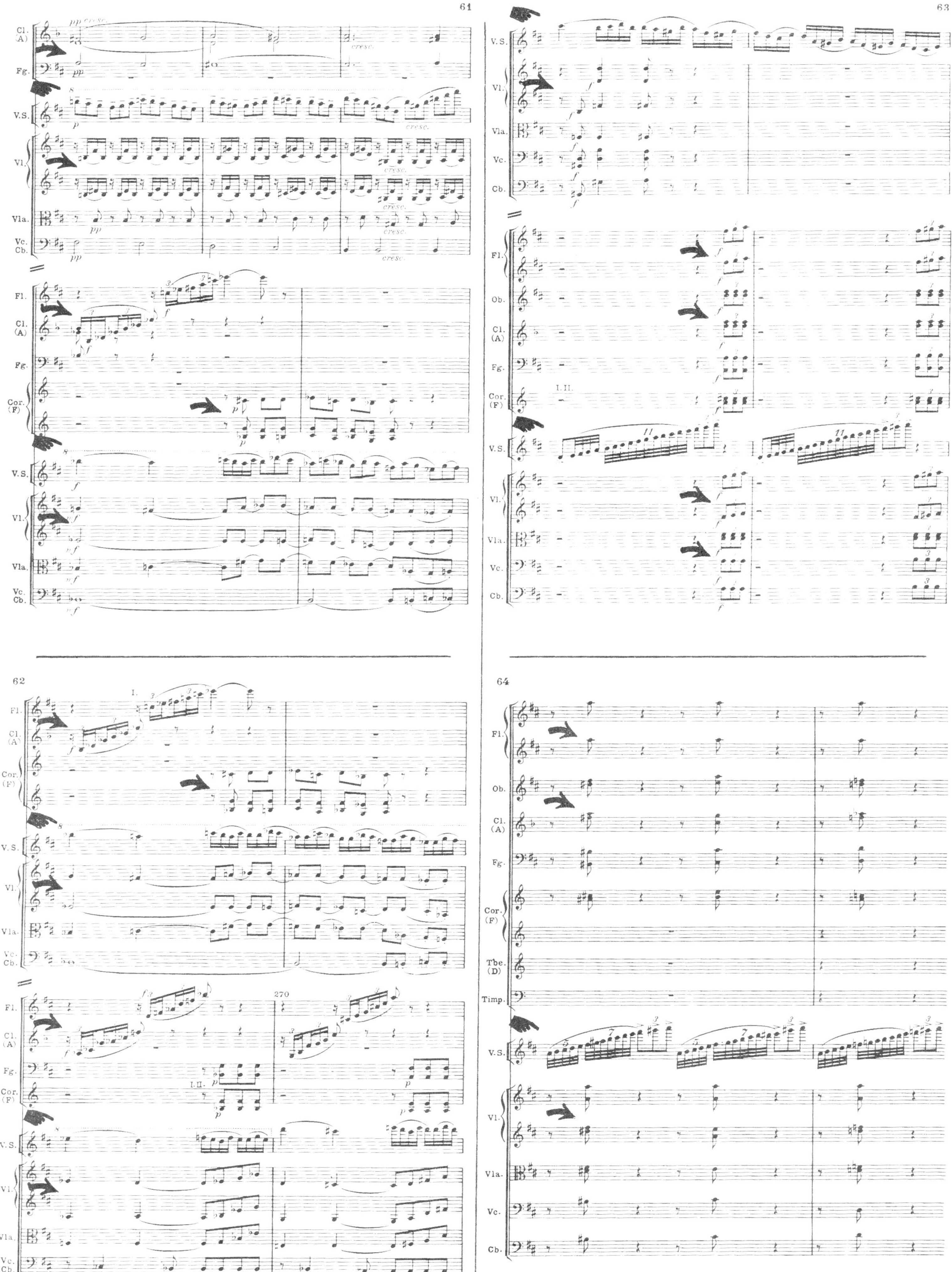
61
Cl. (A)
Fg.
V.S.
Vl.
Vla.
Vc. Cb.
pp cresc.
cresc.
Fl.
Cor. (F)
63
Ob.
I. II.
62
I.
270
64
Tbe. (D)
Timp.

65
Fl.
Ob.
Cl. (A)
Fg.
Cor. (F)
Tbe. (D)
Timp.
V.S.
Vl.
Vla.
Vc.
Cb.
67
Più mosso.
I. II.
66
I. II.
280
68
Poco più lento.
poco a poco cresc.
290

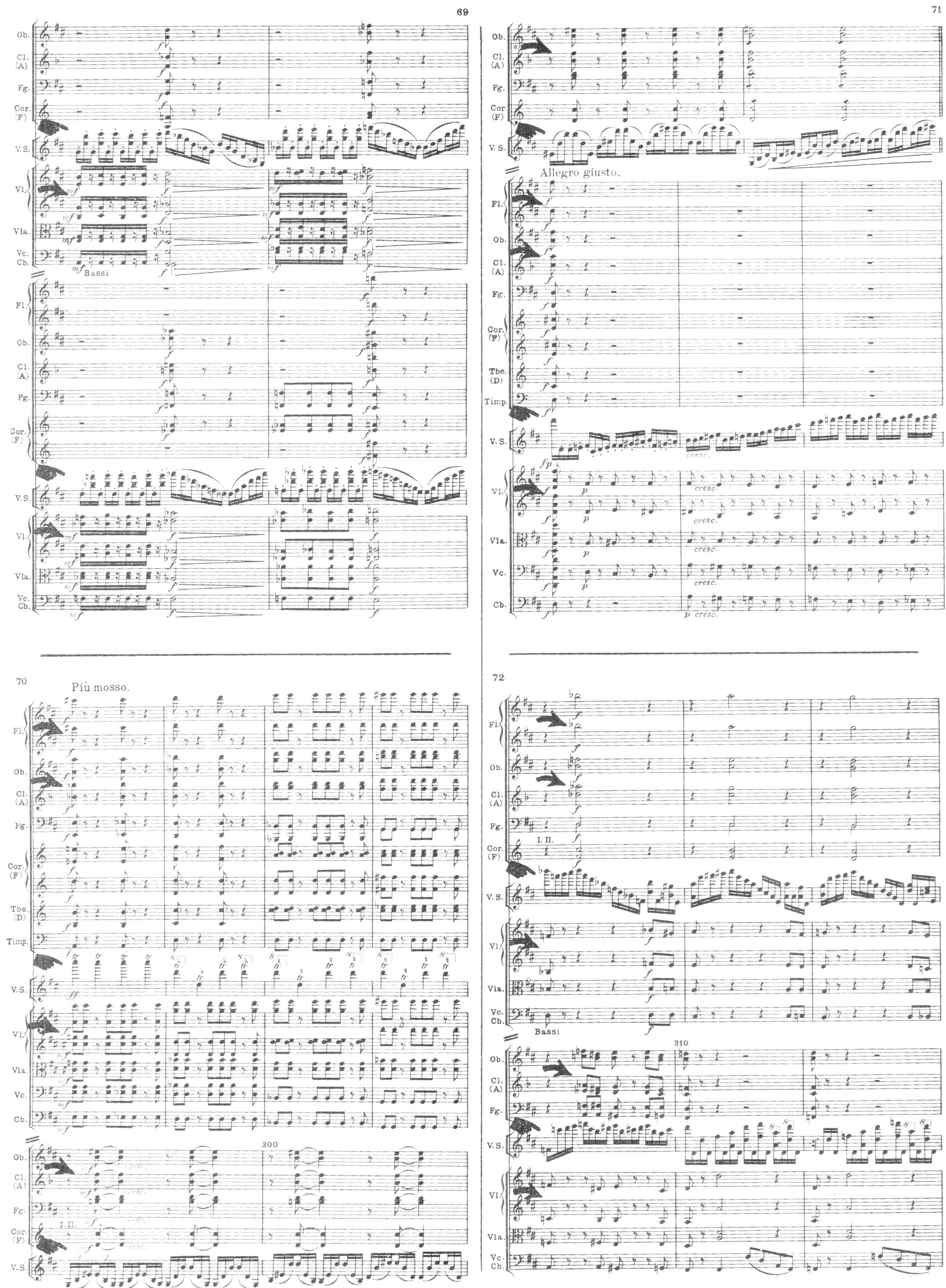

Ob.
Cl. (A)
Fg.
Cor. (F)
V. S.
Vl.
Vla.
Vc. Cb.
Bassi
Fl.
Allegro giusto.
Tbe. (D)
Timp.
cresc.
70
Più mosso.
300
I. II.
72
310

73
75
74
Stringendo.
76
Più mosso.
320
III. IV.
Rmvc.— 257

Fl.
Ob.
Cl. (A)
Fg.
Cor. (F)
Tbe. (D)
Timp.
V. S.
fff
Vl.
Vla.
Vc.
Cb.
78
80
330

II.
Canzonetta.
Andante. ♩= 84.
81
83
2 Flauti.
2 Oboi.
2 Clarinetti in B.
2 Fagotti.
2 Corni in F.
Violino-Solo.
Violino I.
Violino II.
Viola.
Violoncello.
Contrabasso.
10
con sordino
molto espress.
con sordini
82
Iº Solo
20
cresc.
dim.
30
espress.
rit.
40
84
50

85
87
Ob.
Cl. (B)
Fg.
V.S.
Vl.
Vla.
Vc.
Cb.
Fl.
60
80
86
70
88
90
dim.
cresc.
più f
pizz.
arco
mf
f
pp
p cresc.

89
Ob.
Cl. (B)
Fg.
V.S.
Vl.
Vla.
Vc.
100
cresc.
Cor. (F)
mf
pp
90
rallent.
110
Fl.
dim.
riten. molto
Cb.
Attacca subito
III.
91
Finale.
Allegro vivacissimo.
Flauto I.
Flauto II.
2 Oboi.
2 Clarinetti in A.
2 Fagotti.
4 Corni in F.
2 Trombe in D.
Timpani A-D.
Violino-Solo.
Violino I.
Violino II.
Viola.
Violoncello.
Contrabasso.
ff
92
10
Cl. (A)
Tbe. (D)
Timp.

93
20
Fl.
Ob.
Cl. (A)
Fg.
Cor. (F)
Tbe. (D)
Timp.
V. S.
senza sordini
Vl.
Vla.
Vc.
Cb.
30
pizz
arco
pizz.
arco
40
50
dim.
rit.
95
60
pizz.
70
94
Tempo I.
dim.
96
80
cresc.
I. II.

97
99
90
Fl.
Cl. (A)
Cor. (F)
V.S.
Vl.
Vla.
Vc.
Cb.
100
pizz.
110
arco
120
98
Ob.
Fg.
Tbe. (D)
Timp.
130
Bassi

Poco meno mosso.

150

Fl. Ob. Cl. (A) Fg. Cor. (F) Tbe. (D) Timp. V. S. Vl. Vla. Vc. Cb.

p f arco ff arco ff arco ff arco ff p arco ff

Fl. Cl. (A) Fg. V. S. Vl. Vla. Vc. Cb.

p p p p

180 I. II.

Cor. (F) V. S. Vl. Vla. Vc. Cb.

mf cresc. mf mf mf mf

160

Fg. V. S. Vl. Vla. Vc. Cb.

pp pp pp pp

Tempo I.

170

Fl. Cl. (A) Fg. V. S. Vl. Vla. Vc. Cb.

p p p p

Fg. Cor. (F) V. S. Vl. Vla. Vc. Cb.

mf 8 mf mf

190

Ob. Cl. (A) Fg. V. S. Vl. Vla. Vc. Cb.

mf mf mf mf mf

105
Molto meno mosso.
Imo Solo.
p espress.
200
Imo Solo.
p espress.
Ob.
Cl. (A)
Fg.
V.S.
Vl.
Vla.
Vc.
Cb.
107
Quasi andante.
Poco a poco string.
240
Fl.
Tempo I.
Cor. (F)
Timp.
cresc.
dim.
106
210
p espress.
pizz.
Poco a poco rallentando
rall.
220
pp
230
arco
108
250
arco
260
I. II.
mf
dim.

109
111
V.S.
Vl.
Vla.
Vc.
Cb.
Ob.
Cl. (A)
Fl.
Cor. (F)
Fg.
270
280
290
300
310
110
112
I. II.
pizz.
dim.
cresc.

113
Fl.
Ob.
Cl. (A)
Fg.
Cor. (F)
Tbe. (D)
Timp.
V. S.
arco
Vl.
Vla.
Vc.
Cb.
ff
f
115
114
320
116
330
p
cresc.

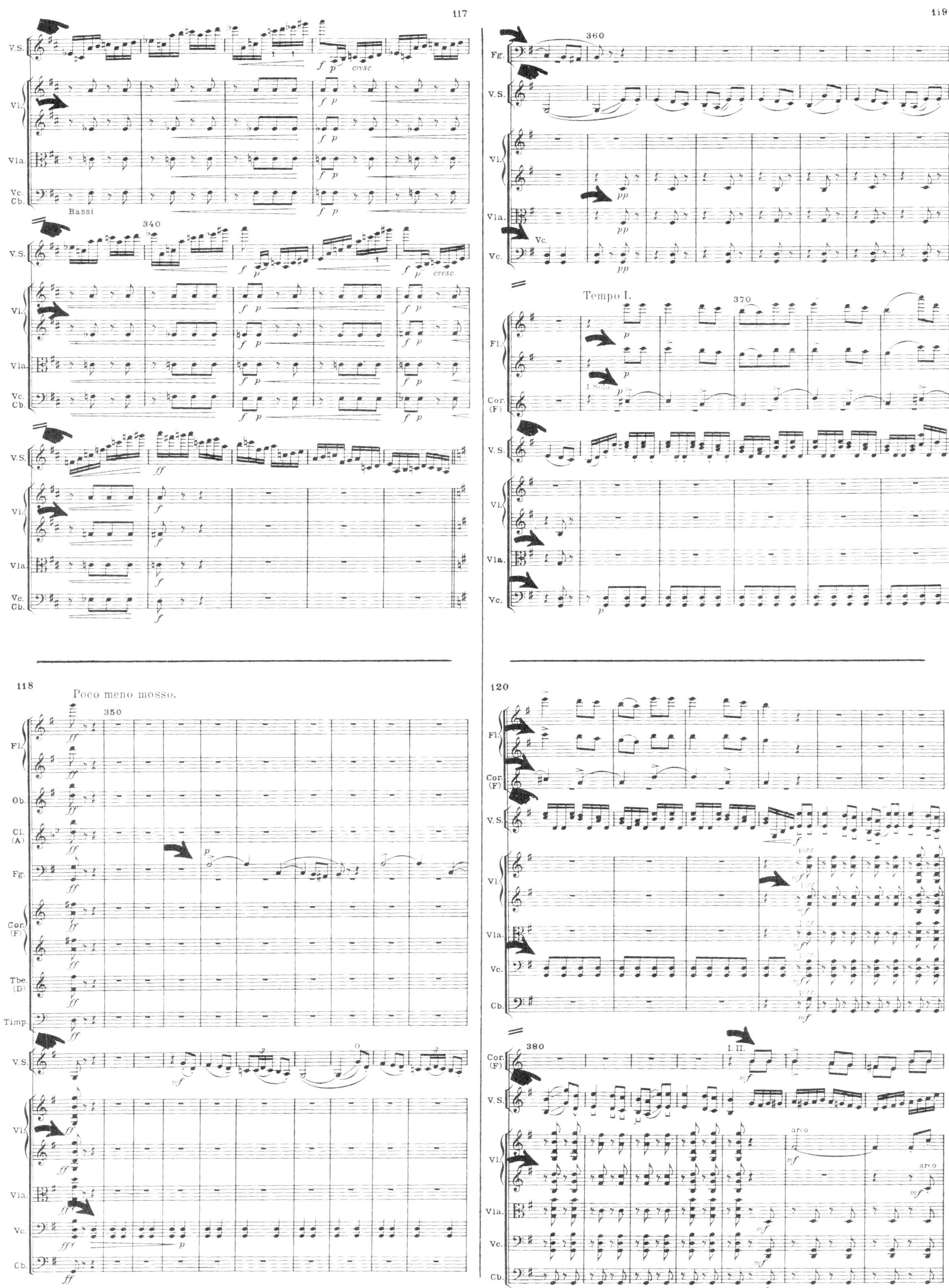
117
119
118
120
V.S.
Vl.
Vla.
Vc.
Cb.
Bassi
340
cresc.
360
Fg.
Tempo I.
370
Fl.
Cor. (F)
I. Solo
Poco meno mosso.
350
Ob.
Cl. (A)
Tbe. (D)
Timp.
pizz.
380
I. II.
arco

Cor. (F)

390

V.S.

Vl.

Vla.

Vc.

Cb.

Fl.

pp

Cl. (A)

Fg.

Cor. (F)

V.S.

Vl.

Vla.

Vc.

Cb.

400 Molto meno mosso.

Fl.

Ob.

p espress.

Cl. (A)

Fg.

V.S.

Vl.

Vla.

Vc.

p

arco

pizz.

410

Fl.

Cl. (A)

Fg.

V.S.

Vl.

Vla.

Vc.

Poco a poco rallentando

420

Fl.

Fg.

V.S.

mf

Vl.

pp

Vla.

Vc.

V.S.

Vl.

Vla.

Vc.

Cb.

arco

430

V.S.

Vl.

Vla.

Vc.

Cb.

Quasi andante.

440

Ob.

Cl. (A)

Fg.

V.S.

Vl.

Vla.

Vc.

Cb.

pp

Cl. (A)
Fg.
V.S.
Vl.
Vla.
Cb.
pp
pizz.
Poco a poco stringendo.
cresc.
ff
Cor. (F)
Ob.
470
p
f
mf
dim.
arco
Tempo I.
Fl.
Tbe. (D)
Timp.
cresc.
480
490

129
130
131
132
500
510
520
530
540
Fl.
Ob.
Cl. (A)
Fg.
Cor. (F)
Tbe. (D)
Timp.
V.S.
Vl.
Vla.
Vc.
Cb.
I.
I. II.
pizz.
arco
poco a poco cresc.
cresc.

133
135
550
560
Fl.
Ob.
Cl. (A)
Fg.
Cor. (F)
Tbe. (D)
Timp.
V. S.
Vl.
Vla.
Vc.
Cb.
mf
cresc.
sempre cresc.
f
134
136
ff

137
570
Fl.
Ob.
Cl. (A)
Fg.
Cor. (F)
Tbe. (D)
Timp.
V. S.
Vl.
Vla.
Vc.
Cb.
139
580
138
140
590
p cresc.

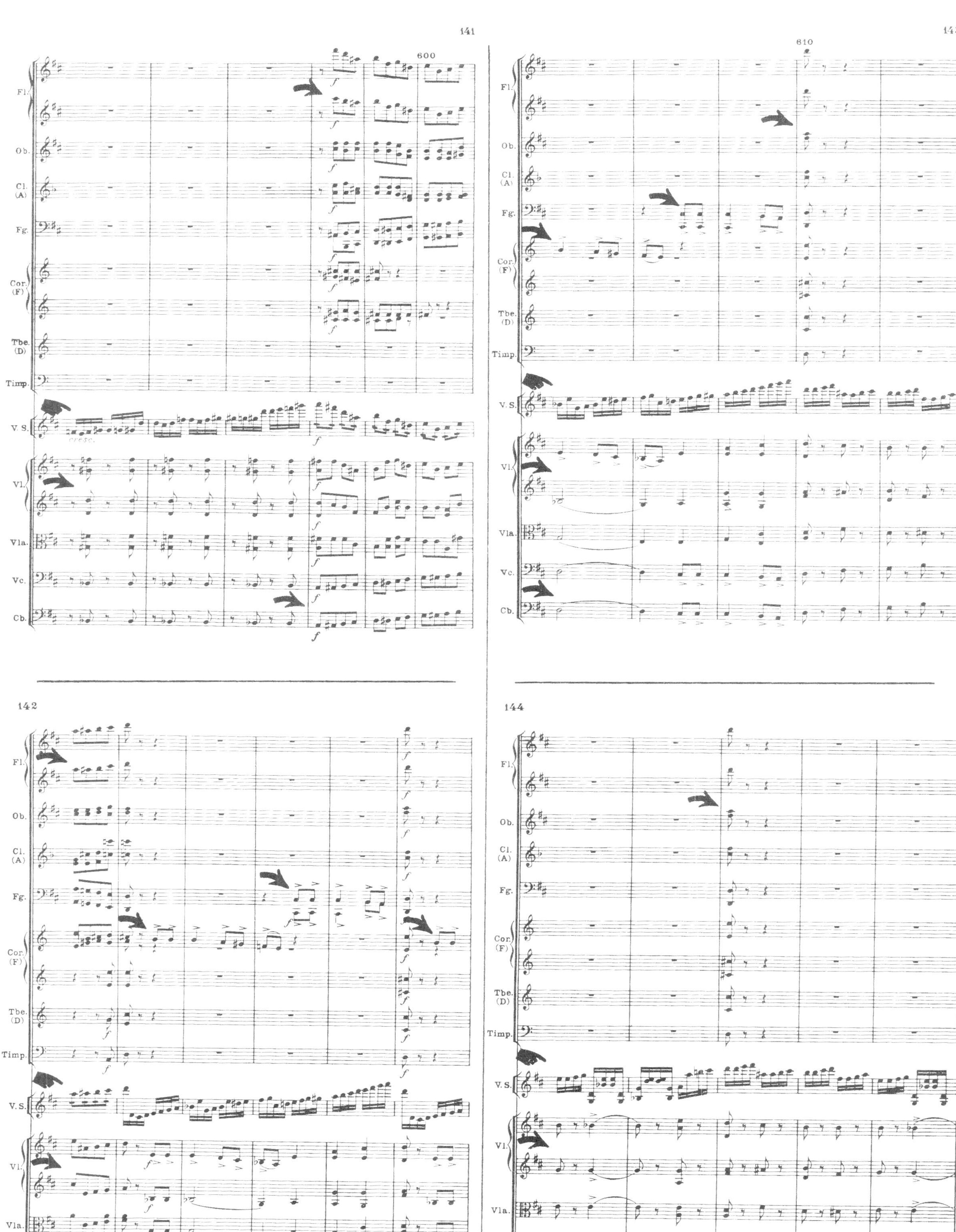

141
600
Fl.
Ob.
Cl. (A)
Fg.
Cor. (F)
Tbe. (D)
Timp.
V. S.
cresc.
Vl.
Vla.
Vc.
Cb.
143
610
142
144

145
620
147
630
Fl.
Ob.
Cl. (A)
Fg.
Cor. (F)
Tbe. (D)
Timp.
V.S.
Vl.
Vla.
Vc.
Cb.
146
148

HENRI VIEUXTEMPS

CONCERTO in D minor, Op. 31

Score P. 277

Henri Vieuxtemps was one of the greatest virtuosos of his time; with Charles de Bériot, who was his teacher, he headed the French school. His compositions for violin and orchestra include six concertos (of which the fourth is presented here), the *Fantasia Appassionata,* Op. 35, and the *Ballade and Polonaise,* Op. 38; all are musically sound and eminently violinistic works which are in the repertoire of most virtuosos.

This concerto was composed during 1849-50 while Vieuxtemps was solo violinist to the Tsar of Russia, and professor of violin at the St. Petersburg Conservatory; he first played it himself at a public concert at Paris in 1851, and Hector Berlioz eulogized it as follows in the *Journal des Débats:* "The concerto presented by Vieuxtemps brought real triumph; he has been proclaimed a remarkable composer, no less an incomparable virtuoso. And this justice has been done him, not only by the public, but by all the expert violinists in Paris who hastened to admire him.

Mme. Camillo Urso played the concerto for the first time in America at a Philharmonic Orchestra concert in Brooklyn, N. Y. on Dec. 14, 1867; the conductor was Theodore Thomas. In addition to the customary three movements, Vieuxtemps added a Scherzo which is optional and often omitted; it is included, however, on the recording by Jascha Heifetz listed on Page 5.

1

Concerto No. 4 in D minor, Op. 31

Henri Vieuxtemps

Andante M.M. ♩ = 80.

Flauto 1mo
Flauto 2do
Oboe 1mo 2do
Clarinetto I in B.
Clarinetto II in B.
Fagotto 1mo 2do
Corno I. II. in D.
Corno 3. 4 in D.
Tromba I. II in D.
Trombone Alto
Trombone Tenor
Trombone Basso
Timpani in A. D.
Violino principale
Violino 1mo
Violino 2do
Viola
Cello
Basso

pp ben sostenuto
p
sempre p
pp ben sost.
pp ben sostenuto

2

3

4

5
7
6
8
Fl. I
Fl. II
Ob. I
Ob. II
Cl. I
Cl. II
Fg. I
Fg. II
Cor. I-II
Cor. III-IV
Tr. I-II
Trom. I
Trom. II
Trom. III
V. P.
V. I
V. II
Vla.
Vc.
Bs.
marc.
marcato
col I.
col Cello
crese
A.

9

espressivo
espressivo
forza
forza

10

mf espress.
mf espress.
cresc.
f espress.
forza
col Bassi

11

Solo
mf dimin.
cresc.
Solo
divisi
pizz.

12

Solo
pizz.
p dim.

13

14

15

16

17

18

20

21

22

23

24

25

Fl. I
Fl. II
Ob. I
Ob. II
Cl. I
Cl. II
Fg. I
Fg. II
Cor. I-II
Cor. III-IV
Tr. I-II
Trom. I
Trom. II
Trom. III
Timp.
V. P.
V. I
V. II
Vla.
Vc.
Cb.
Sul Sol

26

Fl. I
Fl. II
Ob. I
Ob. II
Cl. I
Fg. I
Fg. II
Cor. I-II
Cor. III-IV
Tr. I-II
Trom. I
Trom. II
Trom. III
Timp.
V. P.
V. I
V. II
Vla.
Vc.
Cb.
marcato
Sul Sol
sempre ff

27

Fl. I
Fl. II
Ob. I
Ob. II
Cl. I
Cl. II
Fg. I
Fg. II
Cor. I-II
Cor. III-IV
Tr. I-II
Trom. I
Trom. II
Trom. III
Timp.
V. P.
V. I
V. II
Vla.
Vc.
Cb.
Sul Sol

28

Fl. I
Fl. II
Ob. I
Ob. II
Cl. I
Cl. II
Fg. I
Fg. II
Cor. I-II
Cor. III-IV
Tr. I-II
Trom. I
Trom. II
Trom. III
Timp.
V. P.
V. I
V. II
Vla.
Vc.
Cb.
rit.
a Tempo
dim.

29

Moderato: M.M. ♩.104

Fl. I
Fl. II
Ob. I
Ob. II
Cl. I
Cl. II
Fg. I
Fg. II
Cor. I·II
Cor. III·IV
Tp. I·II
Trom. I
Trom. II
Trom. III
Timp.

V.P. Moderato M.M. ♩.104
pp
con molto espressione
cresc
V. I
ppp
pp
V. II
Vla
p
Vc.
Bs.
pp

30

Fl. I
Fl. II
Ob. I
Ob. II
Cl. I
II
Clar p cresc
p cresc
Fg. I
Fg. II
Cor. I·II
Cor. III·IV
cresc
Tp. I·II
Trom. I
Trom. II
Trom. III
Timp.

V.P.
sf diminu
sf poco cresc
V. I
p
sf
V. II
Vla
p
Vc.
Bs.

31

32

Cadenza
V. P.
a Tempo

a Tempo Tutti
Fl. I
Fl. II
Ob. I
Ob. II
Cl. I
Cl. II
Fg. I
Fg. II
Cor. I-II
Cor. III-IV
Tr. I-II
Trom. I
Trom. II
Trom. III
Timp.
V. P.
rit.
a Tempo
V. I
V. II
col. I
Vla.
Vc.
Bs.

a piacere.
Fl. I
Fl. II
Ob. I
Ob. II
Cl. I
Cl. II
Fg. I
Fg. II
Cor. I-II
Cor. III-IV
Timp.
V. P.
forza
a piacere
V. I
a tempo
Vla.
Vc.
Bs.

Ob. II
Cl. I
Cl. II
Cor. I-II
Cor. III-IV
Solo
dim.
p.
sempre dimin.
Trom. I
Trom. II
Trom. III
Timp.
V. P.
V. I
V. II
Vla.
Vc.
Bs.
piz.

Adagio religioso. M.M. ♩=63.
Flauto 1mo
Flauto 2do
Oboe 1mo
Oboe 2do
Clarinetto I in B.
Clarinetto II in B.
Fagotto 1mo
Fagotto 2do
Corno I II in Es.
Corno 3 4 in B.
Trombe I II in B.
Trombone Alto
Trombone Tenore
Trombone Basso
Timpani in Es. B.
Adagio religioso. M.M. ♩=63.
Violino princip.
Violino 1mo
Violino 2do
Viola
Violoncello
Basso

Fl. I Solo
Fl. II
Ob. I
Ob. II
Cl. I
Cl. II
Fg. I
Fg. II
Cor. I-II
Cor. III-IV
Tr. I-II
Trom. I
Trom. II
Trom. III
Timp.
V.P. Solo
V. I
V. II
Vla.
Vc.
Bs.

Fl. I
Fl. II
Ob. I
Solo
pp dolcissimo
Ob. II
pp dolcissimo
Cl. I
Cl. II
Fg. I
Fg. II
Cor. I-II
Cor. III-IV
Tr. I-II
Trom. I
Trom. II
Trom. III
Timp.
V.P.
V. I
V. II
Vla.
Vc.
Bs.

Fl. I
Fl. II
Ob. I
Ob. II
Cl. I
Cl. II
Fg. I
Fg. II
Cor. I-II
Cor. III-IV
Tr. I-II
Trom. I
Trom. II
Trom. III
Timp.
V.P.
cresc
dimin
V. I
V. II
Vla.
Vc.
Bs.

41

42

Fl. I
Fl. II
Ob. I
Ob. II
Cl. I
Cl. II
Fg. I
Fg. II
Cor. I-II
Cor. III-IV
Tr. I-II
Trom. I
Trom. II
Trom. III
Timp.
V. P.
V. I
V. II
Vla.
Vc.
Bs.
D
mf
pp
p
rit.
a tempo
divisi

43

Fl. I
Fl. II
Ob. I
Ob. II
Cl. I
Cl. II
Fg. I
Fg. II
Cor. I-II
Cor. III-IV
Tr. I-II
Trom. I
Trom. II
Trom. III
Timp.
V. P.
V. I
V. II
Vla.
Vc.
Bs.
p
pp
divisi

44

Fl. I
Fl. II
Ob. I
Ob. II
Cl. I
Cl. II
Fg. I
Fg. II
Cor. I-II
Cor. III-IV
Tr. I-II
Trom. I
Trom. II
Trom. III
Timp.
V. P.
V. I
V. II
Vla.
Vc.
Bs.
mf
f
p
cresc.

45

Fl. I
Fl. II
Ob. I
Ob. II
Cl. I
Cl. II
Fg. I
Fg. II
Cor. I-II
Cor. III-IV
Tr. I-II
Trom. I
Trom. II
Trom. III
Timp.
V. P.
V. I
II
Vla.
Vc.
Bs.

poco cresc.

47

Solo

cresc.

46

cresc.

Solo

48

cresc.

49

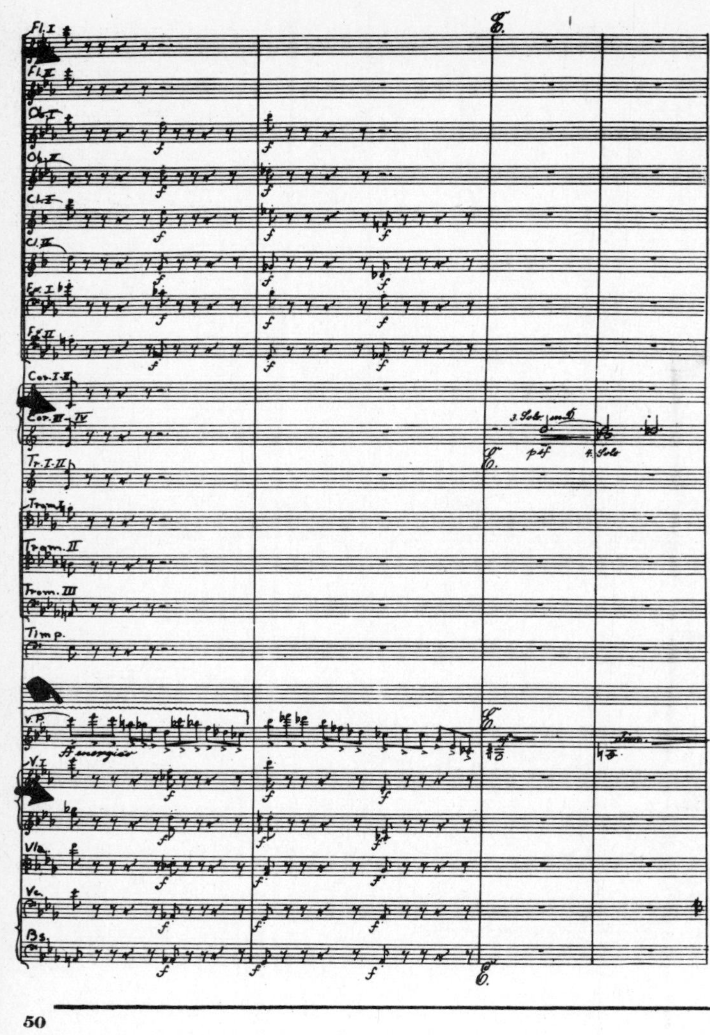
Fl. I
Fl. II
Ob. I
Ob. II
Cl. I
Cl. II
Fg. I
Fg. II
Cor. I-II
Cor. III-IV
Tr. I-II
Timp.
V.P.
V. I
Vla.
Vc.
Bs.

50

Fl. I
Fl. II
Ob. I
Ob. II
Cl. I
Fg. I
Fg. II
Cor. I-II
Harfe
Timp.
V.P.
V. I
Vla.
Bs.

51

Fl. I
Fl. II
Ob. I
Ob. II
Cl. I
Cl. II
Fg. I
Fg. II
Cor. I-II
Harfe
V.P.
V. I
Vla.
Bs.

52

Fl. I
Fl. II
Ob. I
Ob. II
Cl. I
Cl. II
Fg. I
Fg. II
Cor. I-II
Cor. III-IV
Harfe
Timp.
V.P.
a tempo
V. I
V. II
Vla.
Vc.
Bs.

53

Fl. I
Fl. II
Ob. I
Ob. II
Cl. I
Cl. II
Fg. I
Fg. II
Cor. I-II
Cor. III-IV
Harfe
Timp.
V. P.
V. I
Vla.
Vc.
Bs.

55

Fl. I
Fl. II
Ob. I
Ob. II
Cl. I
Cl. II
Fg. I
Fg. II
Cor. I-II
Cor. III-IV
Harfe
Timp.
V. P.
V. I
Vla.
Vc.
Bs.

54

Fl. I
Fl. II
Ob. I
Ob. II
Cl. I
Cl. II
Fg. I
Fg. II
Cor. I-II
Cor. III-IV
Harfe
Timp.
V. P.
V. I
Vla.
Vc.
Bs.

56

Fl. I
Fl. II
Ob. I
Ob. II
Cl. I
Cl. II
Fg. I
Fg. II
Cor. I-II
Cor. III-IV
Harfe
Timp.
V. P.
V. I
V. II
Vla.
Vc.
Bs.

Fl. I
Fl. II
Ob. I
Ob. II
Cl. I
Cl. II
Fg. I
Fg. II
Cor. I-II
Cor. III-IV
cresc.
Harfe
Timp.
V.P.
V. I
Vla.
Vc.
Bs.

Fl. I
Fl. II
Ob. I
Ob. II
Cl. I
Cl. II
Fg. I
Fg. II
Cor. I-II
Cor. III-IV
Harfe
Timp.
V.P.
cresc.
V. I
V. II
Vla.
Vc.
Bs.

58

Fl. I
Fl. II
Ob. I
Ob. II
Cl. I
Cl. II
Fg. I
Fg. II
Cor. I-II
Cor. III-IV
Solo
Harfe
Timp.
V.P.
V. I
Vla.
Bs.

60

Fl. I
Fl. II
Ob. I
Ob. II
Cl. I
Cl. II
Fg. I
Fg. II
Cor. I-II
Solo
Cor. III-IV
Harfe
Timp.
V.P.
V. I
Vla.
Vc.
Bs.

62

64

Scherzo. Vivace. M. M. 𝅗𝅥 = 100.

Flauto 1mo
Flauto 2do
Oboe 1mo
Oboe 2do
Clarinetto 1mo in A.
Clarinetto 2do in A.
Fagotto 1mo
Fagotto 2do
Corno 1. 2. in F.
Corno 3. 4. in D.
Tromba 1. 2. in D.
Timpani A. D.

Scherzo. Vivace. M. M. = 100.

Violino princip.

La seconda volta pp e leggiero

La seconda volta pp

Violino 1mo
Violino 2do
Viola
Violoncello
Basso

arco mf pizz. p

65

Fl. I
Fl. II
Ob. I
Ob. II
Cl. I
Cl. II
Fg. I
Fg. II
Cor. I-II
Cor. III-IV
Tp. I-II
Timp.
V. P.
V. I
Vla.
Vc.
Bs.
arco
pizz.
f
p

67

66

68

70

72

73

Fl. I
Fl. II
Ob. I
Ob. II
Cl. I
Cl. II
Fg. I
Fg. II
Cor. I-II
Cor. III-IV
Tr. I-II
Timp.
V. P.
V. I
V. II
Vla.
Vc.
Bs.

74

Fl. I
Fl. II
Ob. I
Ob. II
Cl. I
Cl. II
Fg. I
Fg. II
Cor. I-II
Cor. III-IV
Tr. I-II
Timp.
V. P.
V. I
V. II
Vla.
Vc.
Bs.

75

Fl. I
Fl. II
Ob. I
Ob. II
Cl. I
Cl. II
Fg. I
Fg. II
Cor. I-II
Cor. III-IV
Tr. I-II
Timp.
V. P.
V. I
V. II
Vla.
Vc.
Bs.

76

Fl. I
Fl. II
Ob. I
Ob. II
Cl. I
Cl. II
Fg. I
Fg. II
Cor. I-II
Cor. III-IV
Tr. I-II
Timp.
V. P.
V. I
V. II
Vla.
Vc.
Bs.
poco a poco cresc.

Fl I
Fl II
Ob I
Ob II
Cl I
Cl II
Fg I
Fg II
Cor I-II
Cor III-IV
Tr I-II
Timp
VP
Vl I
Vl II
Vla
Vc
Bs

Fl I
Fl II
Ob I
Ob II
Cl I
Cl II
Fg I
Fg II
Cor I-II
Cor III-IV
Tr I-II
Timp
VP
Vl I
Vl II
Vla
Vc

G

Fl I
Fl II
Ob I
Ob II
Cl I
Cl II
Fg I
Fg II
Cor I-II
Cor III-IV
Tr I-II
Timp
VP
Vl I
Vl II
Vla
Vc
Bs

Fl I
Fl II
Ob I
Ob II
Cl I
Cl II
Fg I
Fg II
Cor I-II
Cor III-IV
Tr I-II
Timp
VP
Vl I
Vl II
Vla
Vc
Bs

Fl. I
Fl. II
Ob. I
Ob. II
Cl. I
Cl. II
Fg. I
Fg. II
Cor. I-II
Cor. III-IV
Tr. I-II
Timp.
V.P.
V. I
V. II
Vla.
Vc.
Bs.

Fl. I
Fl. II
Ob. I
Ob. II
Cl. I
Cl. II
Fg. I
Fg. II
Cor. I-II
Cor. III-IV
Tr. I-II
Timp.
V.P.
V. I
V. II
Vla.
Vc.
Bs.
cresc.

H
Fl. I
Fl. II
Ob. I
Ob. II
Cl. I
Cl. II
Fg. I
Fg. II
Cor. I-II
Cor. III-IV
Tr. I-II
Timp.
V.P.
V. I
V. II
Vla.
Vc.
Bs.

Fl. I
Fl. II
Ob. I
Ob. II
Cl. I
Cl. II
Fg. I
Fg. II
Cor. I-II
Cor. III-IV
Tr. I-II
Timp.
V.P.
V. I
V. II
Vla.
Vc.
Bs.
cresc.
marcato

Trio Meno mosso
brillante
cresc.
a due
sempre ff
sempre f
dimin.
86
88

89
91
90
92
Fl. I
Fl. II
Ob. I
Ob. II
Cl. I
Cl. II
Fg. I
Fg. II
Cor. I-II
Cor. III-IV
Tr. I-II
Timp.
V. P.
V. I
V. II
Vla.
Vc.
Bs.

93
95
94
96
Fl. I
Fl. II
Ob. I
Ob. II
Cl. I
Cl. II
Fg. I
Fg. II
Cor. I-II
Cor. III-IV
Tp. I-II
Timp.
V. P.
V. I
V. II
Vl.
Vc.
Bs.
p con grazia
p cantando
cresc.
dim.

97
K
Fl. I
Fl. II
Ob. I
Ob. II
Cl. I
Cl. II
Fg. I
Fg. II
Cor. I-II
Cor. III-IV
Tr. I-II
Timp.
V. P.
V. I
V. II
Vla.
Vc.
Bs.
dimin.

99
stringendo
cresc.
Fl. II
Ob. I
Ob. II
Cl. I
Cl. II
Fg. I
Fg. II
stringen-do
Cor. I-II
Cor. III-IV
Tr. I-II
Timp.
strin-gen-do
V. P.
V. I
string.
sin al
V. II
Vla.
Vc.
Bs.
string.

98
strin-gen-do
Fl. I
Fl. II
Ob. I
Ob. II
Cl. I
Cl. II
Fg. I
Fg. II
strin-gen-do
Cor. I-II
Cor. III-IV
Tr. I-II
Timp.
poco cresc.
strin-gen-do
V. P.
V. I
V. II
strin-gen-do
Vla.
Vc.
Bs.

100
Tempo I.
Fl. I
Fl. II
Ob. I
Ob. II
Cl. I
Cl. II
Fg. I
Fg. II
Cor. I-II
Cor. III-IV
Tr. I-II
Timp.
V. P.
Tutti
Tempo I.

105

106

107

108

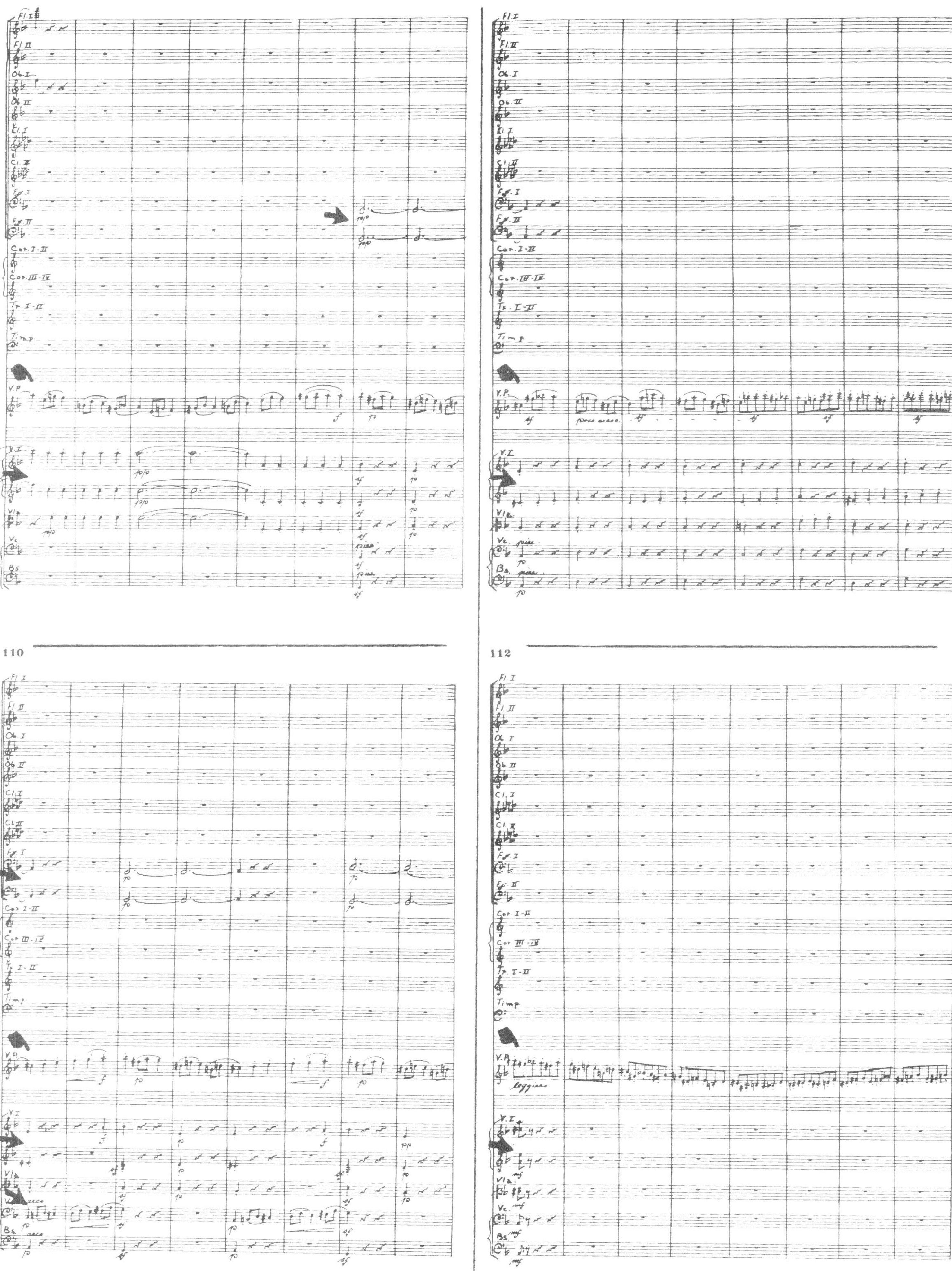
109
111
110
112
Fl. I
Fl. II
Ob. I
Ob. II
Cl. I
Cl. II
Fg. I
Fg. II
Cor. I-II
Cor. III-IV
Tr. I-II
Timp.
V. P.
V. I
Vla
Vc.
Bs.
poco cresc.
leggiero

113
Fl. I
Fl. II
Ob. I
Ob. II
Cl. I
Cl. II
Fg. I
Fg. II
Cor. I-II
Cor. III-IV
Tr. I-II
Timp.
V. P.
V. I
V. II
Vla.
Vc.
Bs.
arco
arco

115
Fl. I
Fl. II
Ob. I
Ob. II
Cl. I
Cl. II
Fg. I
Fg. II
Cor. I-II
Cor. III-IV
Tr. I-II
Timp.
V. P.
V. I
V. II
Vla.
Vc.
Bs.
arco
pizz.
pizz.
arco

114
Fl. I
Fl. II
Ob. I
Ob. II
Cl. I
Cl. II
Fg. I
Fg. II
Cor. I-II
Cor. III-IV
Tr. I-II
Timp.
V. P.
V. I
V. II
Vla.
Vc.
pizz.
pizz.

116
Fl. I
Fl. II
Ob. I
Ob. II
Cl. I
Cl. II
Fg. I
Fg. II
Cor. I-II
Cor. III-IV
Tr. I-II
Timp.
V. P.
V. I
Vla.
Vc.
Bs.
espressivo
arco
arco

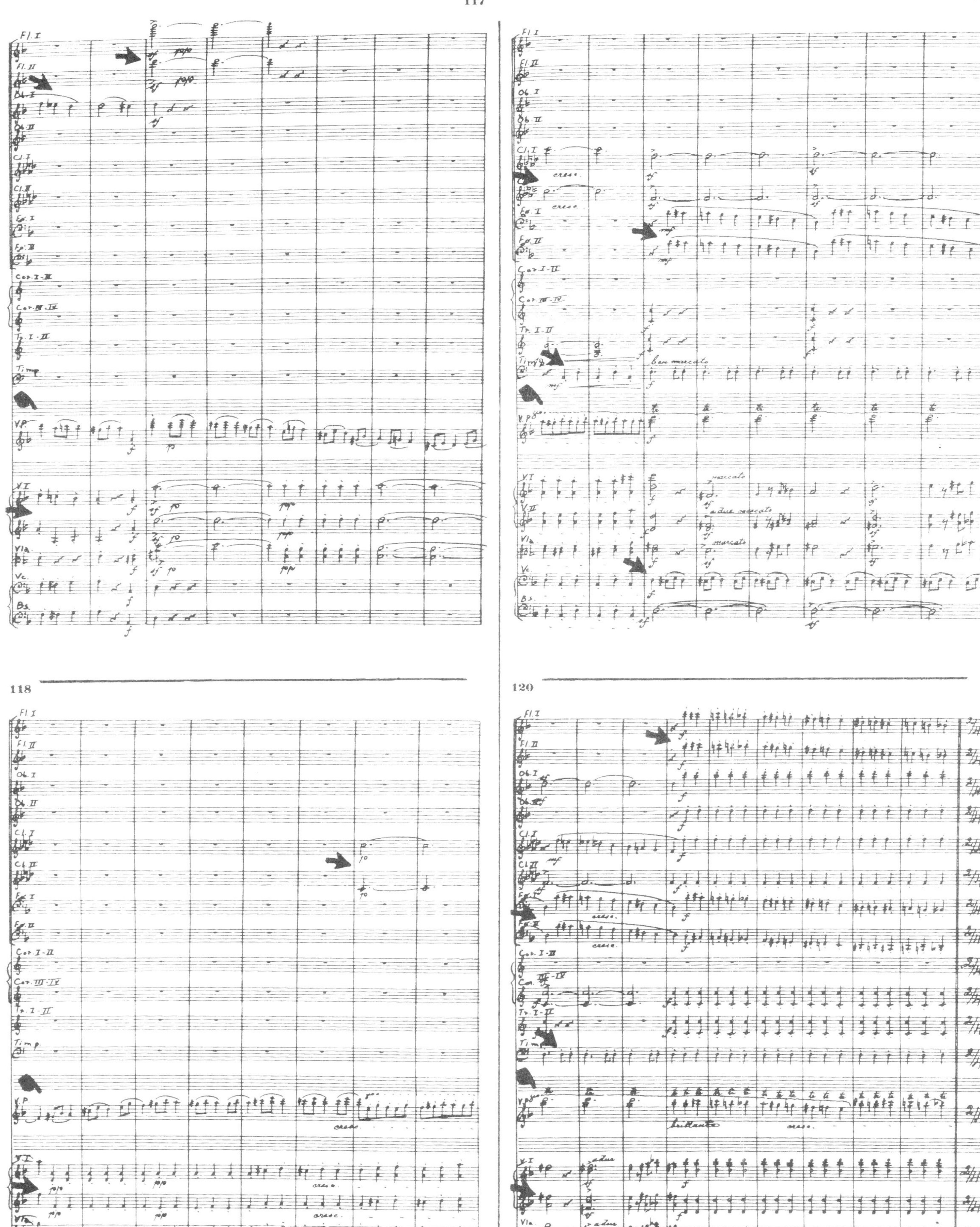

117
119
118
120
Fl. I
Fl. II
Ob. I
Ob. II
Cl. I
Cl. II
Fg. I
Fg. II
Cor. I-II
Cor. III-IV
Tr. I-II
Timp.
V.P.
V. I
V. II
Vla.
Vc.
Bs.
cresc.
ben marcato
marcato
a due marcato
a due
brillante

121
ff sempre

123
tremolo

122
Finale marciale. Andante M.M. ♩= 80.
p con espressione
Tutti.
Finale marciale
Andante M.M. ♩= 80.

124
Allegro M.M. ♩= 80.
energico
Allegro M.M. ♩= 80.

125

127

126

128

129

131

130

132

133

134

135

136

137

138

139

140

141

Fl. I
Fl. II
Ob. I
Ob. II
Cl. I
Cl. II
Fg. I
Fg. II
Cor. I-II
I:
pp
Cor. III-IV
Tr. I-II
Trom. I
Trom. II
Trom. III
Timp.
V.P.
V. I
f p
V. II
marcato
mf
Vla
marcato
mf
Vc.
marcato
marcato
mf
Bs.
col Cello

143

riten. a Tempo

Fl. I
Fl. II
Ob. I
Ob. II
Cl. I
Cl. II
Fg. I
Fg. II
riten. a Tempo
Cor. I-II
Cor. III-IV
Tr. I-II
Trom. I
Trom. II
Trom. III
Timp.
riten. a Tempo
V.P.
sf sf sf
brillante
f p
riten.
V. I
p
V. II
mf p
p
Vla
mf p
p
Vc.
mf p
p
Bs.

142

Fl. I
Fl. II
Ob. I
Ob. II
Cl. I
Cl. II
Fg. I
Fg. II
Cor. I-II
Cor. III-IV
Tr. I-II
Trom. I
Trom. II
Trom. III
Timp.
V.P.
dolce
sempre dolce
V. I
f p
V. II
Vla
mf cantato
Vc.
Bs. f p

144

Fl. I
Fl. II
Ob. I
p
Ob. II
p
Cl. I
Cl. II
Fg. I
Fg. II
Cor. I-II
Cor. III-IV
Tr. I-II
Trom. I
Trom. II
Trom. III
Timp.
V.P.
legno
V. I
V. II
Vla
Vc.
Bs.

145

146

147

148

149
151
150
152
Fl I
Fl II
Ob I
Ob II
Cl I
Cl II
Fg I
Fg II
Cor I-II
Cor III-IV
Tp I-II
Trom I
Trom II
Trom III
Timp
V P
muta in Es
Tutti
cresc.
a due
sempre ff
Vl I
Vl II
Vla
Vc
Bs

153

154

155

156

Fl. I
Fl. II
Ob. I
Ob. II
Cl. I
Cl. II
Fg. I
Fg. II
Cor. I-II
Cor. III-IV
Tr. I-II
Trom. I
Trom. II
Trom. III
Timp.
V. P.
sf
cresc.
f
V. I
cresc.
Vl.
Vc.
cresc.

157

159

158

160

161

162

Fl. I
Fl. II
Ob. I
Ob. II
Cl. I
Cl. II
Fg. I
Fg. II
Cor. I-II
Cor. III-IV
Tr. I-II
Trom. I
Trom. II
Trom. III
V. P.
V. I
V. II
Vle.
Vc.
Bs.
pp dolcissimo
pp dolcissimo
pp dolcissimo
dolce
pizz.

163

164

165
riten. a Tempo
Solo
mf marcato
poco riten. a Tempo
167
cresc.
marcato
poco cresc.
166
marcato
poco cresc.
168
p marcato

Fl. I
Fl. II
Ob. I
Ob. II
Cl. I
Cl. II
Fg. I
Fg. II
Cor. I-II
Cor. III-IV
Tr. I-II
Trom. I
Trom. II
Trom. III
Timp.
V. P.
V. I
Vla.
Vc.
Bs.
marcato
sempre cresc.
poco cresc.

170

172

173

175

174

176

177

Fl. II
Ob. I
Ob. II
Cl. I
Cl. II
Fg. I
Fg. II
Cor. I-II
Cor. III-IV
Tr. I-II
Trom. III
Trom. II
Trom. III
Timp.
V. P.
cresc.
V. I
Vla.
Vc.
Bs.

178

Fl. I
Fl. II
Ob. I
Ob. II
Cl. I
Cl. II
Fg. II
Cor. I-II
Cor. III-IV
Trom. I
Trom. III
Timp.
sempre ff
V. I
Vla.
Vc.
Bs.

179

Ob. I
Ob. II
Cl. I
Cl. II
Fg. I
Fg. II
Cor. I-II
Cor. III-IV
Tr. I-II
Trom. I
Trom. II
Trom. III
Timp.
V. P.
V. I
Vla.
Vc.
Bs.

HENRI WIENIAWSKI

CONCERTO in D minor, Op. 22 *Score P. 323*

Henri Wieniawski, a Polish violinist-composer, spent twelve years (1860-1872) of his professional career, in Russia as solo violinist to the Tsar. In 1872 he toured the United States with Anton Rubinstein; when the latter left to return to Russia, he continued the tour alone as far as California. In 1874 he succeeded Henri Vieuxtemps as professor of violin at the Brussels Conservatory, but resumed concertizing in 1877 although in failing health. During a concert in Berlin, he was obliged to stop in the middle of a concerto, and Joseph Joachim came to his aid by picking up the violin and finishing the performance.

Besides the concerto presented here, Wieniawski composed several important works with orchestral accompaniment for his instrument; they include the Concertos Op. 14 and Op. 22, the Polonaise, Op. 4, the Polonaise, Op. 21, the *Souvenir de Moscou,* Op. 6, the *Scherzo-Tarantelle,* Op. 16, and the superb *Faust Fantasy*, Op. 20. They are compositions of real merit and enduring quality, still heard frequently in concert and broadcast in addition to being recorded by eminent virtuosos.

Concerto in D minor, Op. 22

Henri Wieniawski

1

Allº moderato.

FLAUTI.
OBOI.
CLARINETTI in B. (en Si b.)
FAGOTTI.
CORNI in F. (en FA.)
TROMBI in D. (en RE.)
TROMBONI. ALT.
TENORE.
BASS.
TIMPANI in D u. A. (Re e LA.)
VIOLINO SOLO.

Allº moderato.

VIOLINO. 1.
2.
VIOLA.
VIOLONCELLO. pizz.
CONTRABASSO. pizz.

2

3

4

5

8

Fl. Ob. SOLO. Cl. Fag. Cor. Tromb. 3 Tromb. Timp. Viol. Solo. Viol. 1 2 pizz. arco. Viola. Ve. CB.

6

7

8

9

Animato.
Fl.
Ob.
Cl.
a2.
Animato.
a2.
Fag.
Cor.
Trombi.
3 Tromb.
Timp.
Viol. Solo.
Animato.
pizz.
arco.
Viola.
Animato.
pizz.
arco.
CB. arco.
pizz.

11

Fl.
Ob.
Cl.
Fag.
Cor.
Trombi.
3 Tromb.
1 u. 2.
Timp.
Viol. Solo.
Viola.
Vc.
CB.

10

Fl.
Ob.
a2.
Cl.
a2.
Fag.
a2.
Cor.
Trombi.
3 Tromb.
Timp.
Viol. Solo.
Viola.
Vc.
C.B. arco.

12

Tempo piu tranquillo.
Fl.
Ob.
Cl.
Fag.
Tempo piu tranquillo.
Cor.
Trombi.
3 Tromb.
Timp.
Viol. Solo.
Tempo piu tranquillo.
morendo.
Viol.
Viola.
Vc.
CB.
morendo.

Timp.
B
Viol.Solo.
dolce ma sotto voce.
Viola.
Vc.
CB.
Fl.
Viol.Solo.
Sul A.
pizz.
arco.

Fl.
Ob.
rit.
a tempo.
Cl.
Fag.
Cor.
Trombi.
Timp.
Viol.Solo.
poco rit
Viola.
Vc.
ten.
CB.

Fl.
Ob.
Cl.
Fag.
Solo.
Viol.
Viol. Solo.
à la position.
Viola.
Vc.
CB.

Fl.
C
Ob.
Cl.
Fag.
Cor.
Trombi.
3 Tromb.
Timp.
Viol.Solo.
Viola.
Vc.
pizz.
CB.

17

Fl.
Meno mosso.
Ob.
p
Cl.
Fag.
Cor.
Trombi.
3 Tromb.
Timp.
Viol. Solo.
Sul G.
Meno mosso.
Viol. 1. 2.
p tranquillo
Viola.
Vc.
arco.
p
CB.
arco.

18

Fl.
Ob.
Cl.
1º.
p
Fag.
Cor.
Trombi.
3 Tromb.
Timp.
Viol. Solo.
dolce.
Viol. 1. 2.
p
Viola.
p
Vc.
pizz.
arco.
CB.
arco.
pizz.
arco.

19

Fl.
f
Ob.
p
f
Cl.
p
f
Fag.
p
f
Cor.
Trombi.
3 Tromb.
Timp.
Viol. Solo.
Viol. 1. 2.
Viola.
Vc.
CB.

20

Fl.
a 2.
f
Ob.
Cl.
a 2.
Fag.
Cor.
f
Trombi.
f
3 Tromb.
Timp.
Solo.
f
Viol. 1. 2.
f
p
Viola.
f
p
Vc.
f
p
CB.

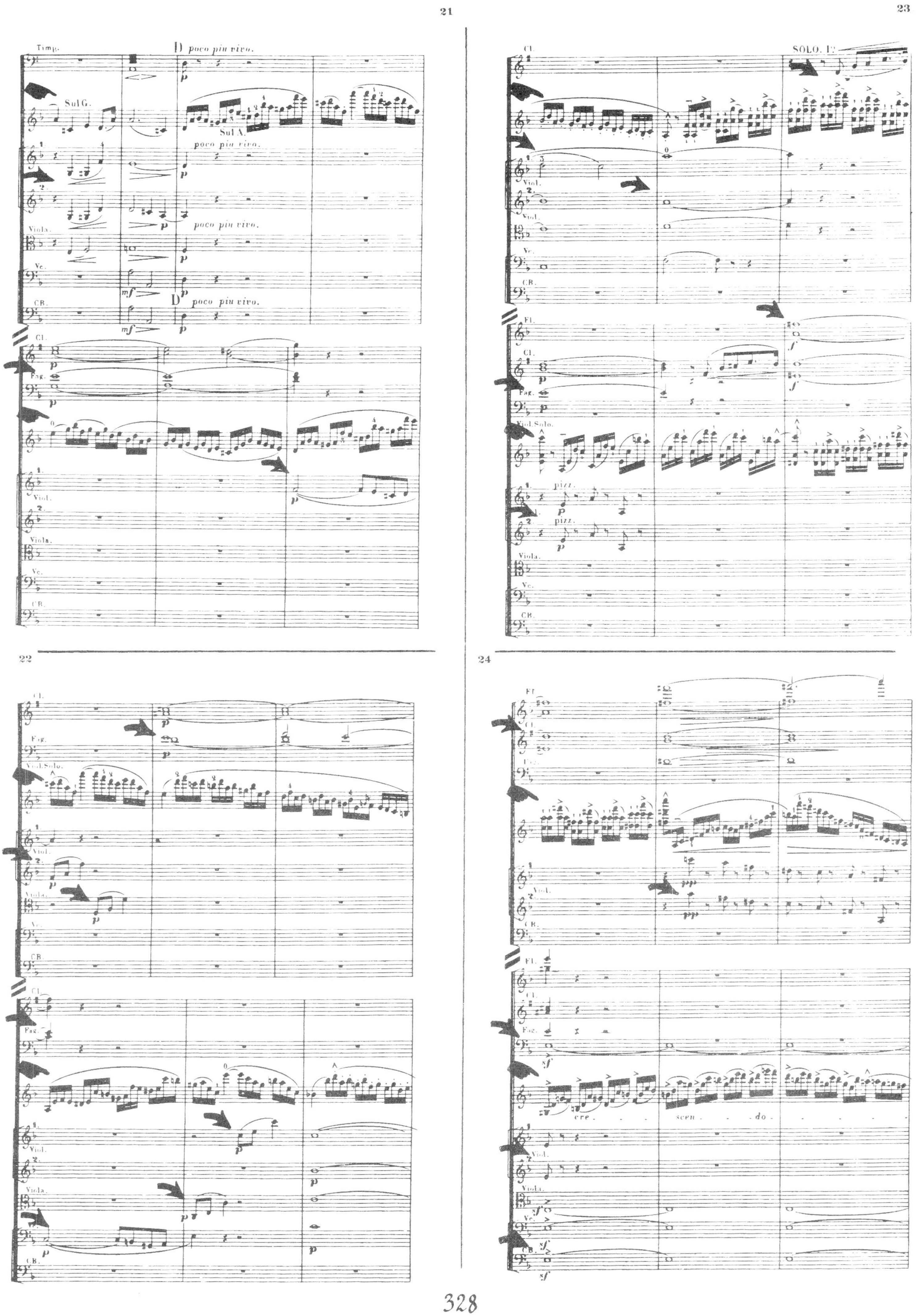

21

Timp.

D poco più vivo.

Sul G.

Sul A.

poco più vivo.

Viola.

Vc.

CB.

Cl.

Fag.

Viol.

22

Cl.

Fag.

Viol. Solo.

Viol.

Viola.

Vc.

CB.

25

Fl.
E
Ob.
Cl.
Fag.
Cor.
Trombi.
3 Tromb.
Timp.
appassionato.
arco.
Viol.
arco.
Viola.
Vc.
CB.

26

Fl.
Ob.
Cl.
Fag.
Cor.
Trombi.
3 Tromb.
Timp.
Viol. Solo.
Viol.
Viola.
Vc.
CB.

27

Fl.
Ob.
Cl.
Fag.
Cor.
Trombi.
3 Tromb.
Timp.
Viol. Solo.
Viola.
Vc.
CB.

28

Ob.
Cor.
Viol. Solo.
Sul G.
Viol.
Viola.
Vc.
CB.
SOLO.
rit.
p simplice.
poco rit.
pizz.

29

Fl.
Ob.
Cl.
Fag.
Cor.
Trombi.
3 Tromb.
Timp.
Viol.
Viola.
Vc.
CB.
arco.

30

F
Fl.
Ob.
Cl.
Fag.
Cor.
Trombi.
3 Tromb.
Timp.
Viol. Solo.
Sul A.
Viol.
Viola.
Vc.
CB. pizz.

31

Fl.
Viol. Solo.
Viol.
Viola.
Vc.
CB. arco.
Fl.
Viol.
Viola.
Vc.
pizz.
CB.
pizz.

32

Fl.
Ob.
Viol. Solo.
Viol.
Viola.
Vc.
arco.
CB.
arco.
SOLO.
Ob.
piu animato.
Viol. Solo.
Sul G.
Viol.
piu animato.
pizz.
Viola.
pizz.
Vc.
piu animato.
pizz.
CB.
pizz.

33
Cor.
SOLO.
Viol.Solo.
Viola.
Vc.
CB.
Cor.
Viola.
Vc.
CB.

34
Fl.
G
Ob.
Cl.
Fag.
Cor.
Trombi.
3 Tromb.
Timp.
Sul G.
G
pizz.
Viola.
Vc.
CB.

35
Fl.
Ob.
Cl.
Fag.
Cor.
Trombi.
3 Tromb.
Timp.
arco.
arco.
Viola.
arco.
arco.
Vc.
CB.

36
Fl.
Cl.
Fag.
Sul D.G.
Viola.
Vc.
CB. arco.
Viol.
Viola.
Vc.
CB.

37

Fl.
Viol. Solo.
Sul D.
Viol.
pizz.
Viola.
Vc.
CB.

38

Fl.
Ob.
Cl.
Fag.
Cor.
SOLO.
Trombi.
3 Tromb.
Timp.
Viol. Solo.
arco.
Viola. arco.
Vc.
pizz.
CB.

39

Fl.
Ob.
Cl.
Fag.
Cor.
Trombi.
3 Tromb.
Timp.
Viol.
Viola.
Vc.
CB.

40

H
Fl.
Ob.
Cl.
Fag.
Cor.
Trombi.
3 Tromb.
Timp.
Viol. Solo.
H
pizz.
Viola
arco.
Vc.
arco.
CB.
pizz.

Fl.
Ob.
Cl.
Fag.
Cor.
Trombi.
3 Tromb
Timp.
restez.
Viol.
arco.
Viola.
Vc.
CB.
arco.

42

Fl.
Ob.
Cl.
Fag.
Cor.
Trombi.
3 Tromb.
Timp.
Viol.
Viola.
Vc.
CB.

Fl.
Ob.
Cl.
Fag.
Cor.
Viol.Solo.
Viol.
Fl.
Ob.
Cl.
Fag.
Cor.
Viol.Solo.
Viol.

44

Fl.
TUTTI.
Ob.
Cl.
a 2.
Fag.
Cor.
Trombi.
3 Tromb.
Timp.
Viol.Solo.
TUTTI.
TUTTI.
Viol.
Viola.
Vc.
CB.

45
Fl.
Ob.
Cl.
a 2.
Fag.
Cor.
Trombi.
3 Tromb.
Timp.
Viola

47
Fl.
J
Ob.
Cl.
Fag.
Cor.
Trombi.
3 Tromb.
Timp.
Viol. Solo.
Viola.
Ve.
CB.
pizz.

46
Fl.
a 2.
Ob.
Cl.
Fag.
Cor.
Trombi.
3 Tromb.
Timp.
Viol. Solo.
Viola.
Vc.
CB.

48
Fl. a 2.
Ob.
Cl.
Fag.
Cor. a 2.
Trombi.
3 Tromb.
1 u. 2.
Timp.
Viol. Solo.
Viol.
Viola.
Vc.
CB. arco.
pizz.
arco.

49

Fl.
1º p
Ob.
Cl.
1º
p
Fag.
Cor.
f
Trombi.
3 Tromb.
Timp.
Viol. Solo.
1.
Viol.
2.
tranquillo.
cresc.
p
p
Viola.
p
Vc.
p
pizz.
CB.

50

Fl.
a 2.
Ob.
Cl.
Fag.
Cor.
Trombi.
3 Tromb.
Timp.
Viol. Solo.
1.
2.
cresc.
Viola.
Vc.
CB.
arco.

51

Fl.
a 2.
Ob.
Cl.
a 2.
Fag.
a 2.
Cor.
Trombi.
3 Tromb.
Timp.
Viol. Solo.
1.
pizz.
p
arco.
2.
pizz.
p
arco.
Viola.
pizz.
arco.
Vc.
pizz.
arco.
CB.
pizz.
arco.

52

Fl.
p
Ob.
ff
p
ff
Cl.
ff
p
ff
Fag.
ff
p
ff
Cor.
ff
p
ff
Trombi.
3 Tromb.
Timp.
Viol. Solo.
1.
p
2.
p
Viola.
p
p
Vc.
p
CB.
p

53

54

55

56

Romance.

Andante non troppo.

Fl.

Ob.

Cl.

Fag.

Cor.

Trombi. Tacet.

3 Tromb. Tacet.

Timp. Tacet.

Viol. Solo.

Andante non troppo.

Viol. 1, 2

Viola.

Vc.

CB.

rit.
Viol.
rit.
Viola.
rit.
Vc.
CB.
arco. rit.
Ob.
SOLO.
p
Cl.
p
p
Fag.
p
Cor.
p
espress.
pp dol.
pp
Viola.
Vc.
CB. pizz.
pizz.

58

Fl. A
Ob
Cl.
rit.
Fag.
rit.
Cor.
poco rit.
A
rit.
pp
pp
Viola.
rit.
Vc.
pizz.
CB.
pizz.
rit.

Cl. a tempo.
a tempo.
Viol.
Viola. arco.
p
p
Vc.
CB. a tempo.
Cl.
a tempo.
rit.
p
Fag.
p
p
rit.
Cor.
espressivo.
a tempo.
espress.
Viol.
poco rit.
p
pp
rit.
Viola.
Vc.
CB.
arco.
rit.
pizz.

60

Fl.
animato.
SOLO.
p
Ob.
p
SOLO.
Cl. p
Fag.
animato.
Cor.
animato.
animato.
Viol.
Viola.
animato.
Vc.
arco.
CB.
arco.
animato.

61

Fl.
p
Ob.
p
Cl.
p
Fag.
Cor.
1
pizz.
2
Viola.
Vc.
CB.

63

Fl.
mf
Ob.
Cl.
1º
Fag.
Cor.
Viol. Solo.
1.
cresc.
2.
cresc.
Viola.
cresc.
Vc.
CB.

62

Fl.
B
Ob.
animato.
Cl.
animato.
Fag.
p
p
Cor.
p
1º
Viol. Solo.
p
1.
arco.
B
p
animato.
2. pizz.
arco.
Viola.
pizz.
animato.
p
Vc. pizz.
arco.
p
CB.
pizz.
arco.
p
animato.

64

Fl.
poco rit.
rit.
Ob.
Cl.
Fag.
Cor.
1.
poco rit.
poco rit.
2.
poco rit.
Viola.
Vc.
ff
CB.
poco rit.
ff

65

Fl.
Ob.
a tempo.
Cl.
pp
Fag.
pp
Cor.
Viol. Solo.
dolce.
a tempo.
pp dolcissimo.
2.
pp
Viola.
pp
Vc.
pp dolcissimo.
a tempo.
CB.
pizz.
pp

66

Fl.
Ob.
SOLO.
p
Cl.
Fag.
Cor.
Viol. Solo.
1.
Viol.
2.
Viola.
Vc.
CB.
arco.
p

67

Fl.
Ob.
rit.
p
Cl.
rit.
Fag.
rit.
Cor.
ff
1.
poco rit.
Viol.
2.
Viola.
rit.
Vc.
rit.
CB.

68

Fl.
Ob.
SOLO.
Cl.
rit.
Fag.
Cor.
rit.
p
molto rit.
1.
p
rit.
2.
p
Viola.
Vc.
rit.
CB.
rit.

69

Fl. a tempo.
p
Ob.
p
p
Cl.
p
Fag.
p
Cor.
a tempo.
1.
pizz.
a tempo.
2.
pizz.
pp
Viola.
pizz.
Vc.
a tempo.
CB.
p

71

Fl. Allegro con fuoco.
Ob.
f
Cl.
Fag.
Cor.
Trombi.
3 Tromb.
Timp.
Allegro con fuoco.
arco.
Viola.
Vc.
CB.

70

Fl.
pp
Ob.
pp
Cl.
pp
Fag.
Cor.
dim.
p
1.
pizz.
p
2.
pizz.
pizz.
Viola
p
Vc.
pp
CB.
pp

72

Fl.
Ob.
Cl.
Fag.
Cor.
Trombi.
3 Tromb.
Timp.
1.
2.
Viola.
Vc.
CB.

Fl.
Ob.
Cl.
Fag.
Cor.
Trombi.
3 Tromb.
Timp.
Cadenza.
cresc.
Viola.
Vc.
CB.

Viol Solo.
leggiero.
Viol.
Viola.
Vc.
CB.
rit.
dim.

Allegro moderato. (à la Zingara.)
Fl.
Ob.
SOLO.
Cl.
Fag.
Cor.
Trombi.
3 Tromb.
Timp.
Allegro moderato. (à la Zingara.)
pizz.
Viol.
Viola.
Vc. pizz.
CB. pizz.

Fl.
Ob.
Cl.
Fag.
Cor.
Trombi.
3 Tromb.
Timp.
Viola.
Vc.
CB.

77

Fl.
Ob.
Cl.
Fag.
Cor.
Trombi.
3 Tromb.
Timp.
arco.
Viol.
arco.
Viola.
arco.
Vc.
arco.
pizz.
CB.

78

2. pizz.
Viola.
pizz.
Vc.
CB.
Fl.
SOLO.
Ob.
SOLO.
Cl.
Fag.
tranquillo.
1. pizz.
2.
Viola.
Vc.
pizz.
CB.

79

Fl.
Ob.
Cl.
Fag.
Cor.
Trombi.
3 Tromb.
Timp.
arco.
arco.
Viola.
Vc.
arco.
CB.

80

Fl.
Ob.
Cl.
Fag.
Cor.
Trombi.
3 Tromb.
Timp.
Viola.
arco.
Vc.
pizz.
CB.
pizz.

81

A TUTTI.
Fl.
Ob.
Cl.
Fag.
Cor.
Trombi.
SOLO.
3 Tromb.
Timp.
TUTTI.
cre - scen - do
A TUTTI.
Viol.
Viola.
arco.
Vc.
arco.
CB.
arco.

82

Fl.
Ob.
Cl.
Fag.
a 2.
Cor.
Trombi.
3 Tromb.
Timp.
Viol.
Viola.
Vc.
CB.

83

Fl.
Ob.
Cl.
Fag.
a 2.
Cor.
Trombi.
3 Tromb.
Timp.
Viol.
Viola.
Vc.
CB.

84

Fl.
Ob.
Cl.
Fag.
Cor.
a 2.
Trombi.
3 Tromb.
Timp.
Viola.
Vc.
CB.

85

Fl.
Ob.
Cl.
Fag.
Cor.
Trombi.
3 Tromb.
Timp.
Viola.
Vc.
CB.
rit.
p tranquillo.
tranquillo.
Sul A.
poco a poco rit.
poco piu tranquillo.
Tempo tranquillo.
pizz.

86

Fl.
Ob.
Cl.
Fag.
Cor.
Trombi.
3 Tromb.
Timp.
Viol.
Viola.
Vc.
CB.

87

Fl.
Ob.
Cl.
Fag.
Cor.
Trombi.
3 Tromb.
Timp.
appassionato.
cre -
arco.
dol.
pizz.
Viola.
Vc.
CB.

88

Fl.
Ob.
Cl.
Fag.
Cor.
Trombi.
3 Tromb.
Timp.
scen - do
ff molto appassionato
Viola.
arco.
Vc.
CB.

89

Fl.
Ob.
Cl.
Fag.
Cor.
Trombi.
3 Tromb.
Timp.
Viola.
Vc.
pizz.
arco.
CB. pizz.
mf
p

90

Fl.
Ob.
Cl.
Fag.
Cor.
Trombi.
3 Tromb.
Timp.
Viola.
Vc. pizz.
CB. pizz.
B
a tempo.
poco rit.
rit.
Sul G.
du talon.
molto vibrato.
saltando.
arco.
fp
p

91

Cor.
Viol.
Viola.
Vc.
CB.
pizz.
p

92

Fag.
Viola.
Vc.
CB.
pizz.
Cor.
CB. pizz.
p

93

Timp.
Viol. Solo.
Viola.
Vc.
CB.
arco.
pp
Fl.
Ob.
SOLO.
p
Cor. SOLO.
Timp.
pizz.
Viol.
Viola. pizz.
Vc.
CB.

95

Fl.
Ob.
rit.
Cl.
Fag.
Cor.
2° SOLO.
Trombi.
3 Tromb.
Timp.
pp
cresc.
poco rit. e dim.
arco.
Viol.
Viola.
Vc.
CB.

94

Fl.
C
Ob.
Cl.
Fag.
Cor.
Trombi.
3 Tromb.
Timp.
Solo.
Viol.
Viola.
Vc.
CB.

96

Fl.
Ob.
Cl.
Fag.
Cor.
Trombi.
pp
3 Tromb.
Timp.
Solo.
f
pizz.
Viol.
Viola.
Vc.
arco.
CB.

97

Fl.
Ob.
Cl.
Fag.
Cor.
Trombi.
3 Tromb.
Timp.
Viol.
arco.
pizz.
Viola.
Vc.
CB.

98

Fl.
Ob.
Cl.
Fag.
Cor.
Trombi.
3 Tromb.
Timp.
Viol.
arco.
Viola.
Vc.
CB.

99

Fl.
a piacere.
Ob.
Cl.
Fag.
Cor.
Timp.
Solo.
Viol.
Viola.
Vc.
Viol. Solo.
Vc. pizz.
CB. pizz.
arco.
pizz.

100

Molto moderato.
Fag.
Cor.
Timp.
Sul G.
Viol.
Viola.
Vc.
CB.

101

103

102

104

105
pp
Fl.
D
Ob.
Cl.
Fag.
Cor.
p
Trombi.
3 Tromb.
Timp.
appassionato
arco.
D
molto
2.
pizz.
arco.
Viola.
Ve.
arco.
CB.
arco.

107
1º tempo moderato.
Fl.
Ob.
rit.
Cl.
Fag.
Cor.
rit.
Trombi.
3 Tromb.
Timp.
rit.
1º tempo moderato.
pizz.
Viola.
pizz.
pp
Vc.
CB.

106
Fl.
Ob.
Cl.
Fag.
Cor.
sf
Trombi.
3 Tromb.
Timp.
appassionato
2.
Viola.
Vc.
pizz.
arco.
CB.
pizz.
pizz.

108
Fl.
Cor.
Viol. Solo.
2.
Viola.
CB.
Fl.
Cl.
Fag.
Cor.
arco.
p
Viola.
arco.
Vc.
CB.

109

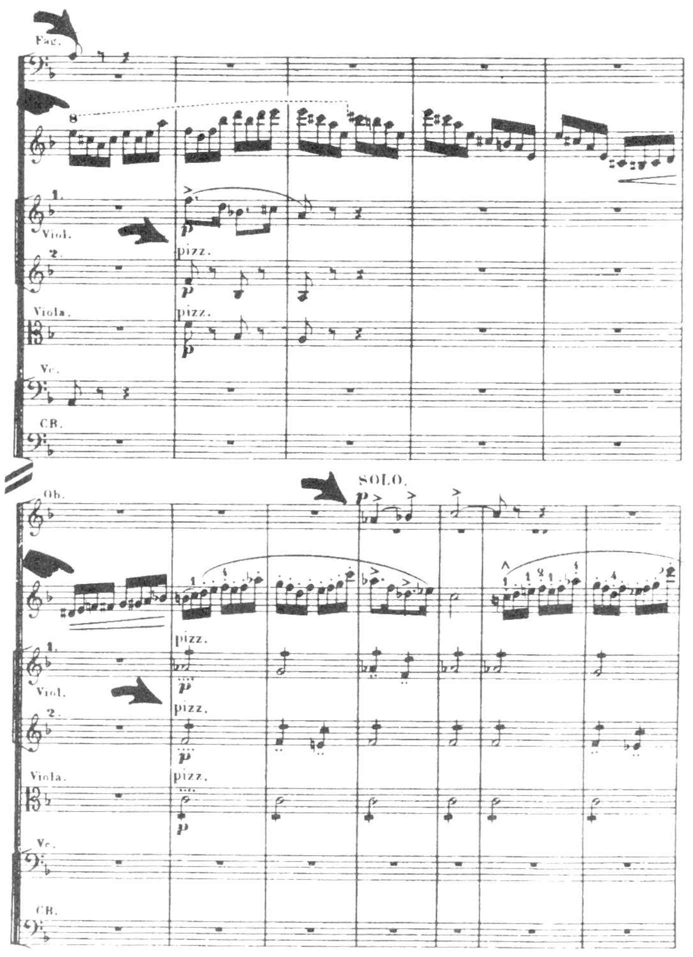

Fag.

Viol. 1. 2. pizz.

Viola. pizz.

Vc.

CB.

Ob. SOLO.

Viol. 1. 2. pizz.

Viola. pizz.

Vc.

CB.

110

Fl.

Ob.

Cl.

Viol. Solo.

arco.

Viola.

Vc.

Fl.

Cl.

Fag.

Viol. Solo.

Viola arco.

Vc. pizz.

CB.

111

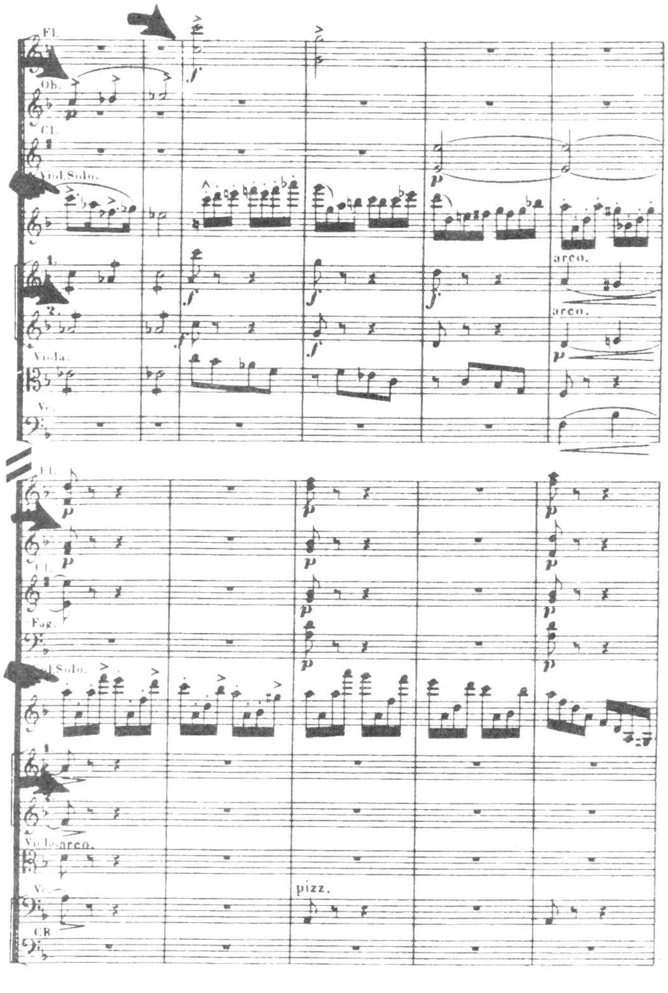

112

113

115

114

116

117

118

Fl.
f
ff
Ob.
Cl.
ff
Fag.
ff
Cor.
ff
Tromb.
ff
ff
3 Tromb.
f
ff
Timp.
f
ff
Viola.
f
Vc.
C.B.